CLEAN-UP PROCEDURES
FOR MOLD IN
HOUSES

D1396521

Prepared for CMHC by

James Scott, PhD, CCM (ARM) (Academic and Research Microbiologist, Canadian College of Microbiologists)

Dr. Scott is Assistant Professor of Environmental and Medical Mycology in the Department of Public Health Sciences, the Faculty of Medicine, the University of Toronto. He is a diplomate of the Canadian College of Medical Microbiologists, 2003. Dr. Scott is also chief executive officer of Sporometrics Inc., Toronto, an environmental mycology laboratory.

CMHC project manager

Dr. Virginia Salares, Senior Researcher, Housing Technology, CMHC

CMHC offers a wide range of housing-related information.
For details, call 1 800 668-2642 or visit our home page at www.cmhc.ca

Cette publication est aussi disponible en français sous le titre :
Méthodes d'élimination de la moisissure dans les maisons (61279)

The information contained in this publication represents current research results available to CMHC and has been reviewed by experts in the housing industry. Readers are advised to evaluate the information, materials and techniques cautiously for themselves and to consult appropriate professional resources to determine whether information, materials and techniques are suitable in their case. The drawings and text are intended as general practice guides only. Project and site-specific factors of climate, cost, esthetics and so on must be taken into consideration. Any photographs in this book are for illustration purposes only and may not necessarily represent currently accepted standards.

National Library of Canada cataloguing in publication data

Main entry under title:

Clean-up procedures for mold in houses

Rev. ed.
Issued also in French under title: Méthodes d'élimination de la moisissure dans les maisons.
ISBN 0-660-19227-6
Cat. no. NH15-91/2003E

1. Dampness in buildings.
2. Indoor air pollution – Health aspects.
3. Housing and health.
I. Canada Mortgage and Housing Corporation.

RA577.5C53 2003   613'.5   C2003-980340-6

Printed in Canada
Produced by CMHC

TABLE OF CONTENTS

GLOSSARY

Air leakage: undesirable leakage of warm, moist air from the dwelling-space of a house into the attic, which risks causing condensation in the attic or may lead to ice damming on the roof.

Caulking: the use of caulk, a sealant and filler, to close and waterproof the seams between two elements of a house, such as a tile wall and a bathtub.

Cladding: material (wood, vinyl, metal, masonry or stucco) that covers to exterior wall of a building.

Condensation: the process whereby warm water vapour in the air assumes liquid form on a cold surface; also, the resulting liquid water.

Control joints: spaces or gaps deliberately placed on the exterior surface of a house to allow for thermal expansion.

Dehumidifier: a device for removing humidity from the air within an enclosed space, typically a basement.

Desiccant: a chemical substance that absorbs water and may be used to remove humidity from a small, enclosed space such as a plastic storage bin.

Detail: minor decorations on a building.

Disinfectant: a chemical liquid that kills but not necessarily removes germs, including mold.

Downspout: a vertical (often metal) pipe on the exterior of a house designed to direct water either into the sewer system or away from the house.

Drywall: a building material for finishing interior walls, consisting of sheets of gypsum covered by paper.

Dust mite: a microscopic, insect-like animal that feeds on one of the main components of house dust, i.e., the flakes of skin shed by people or animals; they typically live in beds. Dust mites also feed on fungal spores and other debris.

Eaves: the part of the roof that extends beyond the walls of the house.

Eavestroughs: horizontal (often metal) gutters lining the eaves of a roof, designed to collect water that runs down the roof and to release it into the downspouts.

Efflorescence: the process whereby salt dissolved in moisture that migrates through concrete or masonry crystallizes on the dry side of the wall, producing a somewhat fuzzy accumulation that may be mistaken for mold; also refers to the accumulation itself.

Flashing: a metal strip used to prevent water penetration at the juncture of two elements of a building, such as a wall and roof.

Foxing: a brownish mottling or discoloration on (usually old) paper, caused by damp, though not necessarily associated with mold.

Fungi (singular Fungus): a biological Kingdom, with origins midway between those of plants and animals, of spore-producing organisms that feed on organic matter; members of this kingdom include mushrooms, yeasts and molds.

HEPA filter: High-Efficiency Particulate Air filter used in air purifiers and sophisticated vacuum cleaners to trap the tiny particles normally missed by ordinary vacuum cleaners.

Humidifier: a device for increasing the humidity in an enclosed space considered too dry.

Hygrometer: a device to measure relative humidity.

Hyphae: tiny filaments used by molds to invade and to help transform, both by mechanical and chemical means, damp organic matter into nutrients digestible by the molds.

Ice damming: a process whereby excessive heat from a house causes ice on the roof to melt and roll down to the eaves where it refreezes (since eaves are colder than the rest of the roof) blocking subsequent water, which may stand on the roof behind the **ice dam** and cause leaks.

Lath: thin flat strips of wood arranged in a framework to help support a layer of plaster applied over them.

Mildew: properly speaking, a small group of fungi that cause disease in plants, producing powdery white blotches on leaves. The term is sometimes used commonly (and incorrectly) to refer to certain household molds.

Millwork: cabinetry.

Mold: a sub-group of the Kingdom of Fungi who colonize damp organic matter and in so doing, frequently cause trouble to humans.

Mycology: the study of fungi, including molds.

Plaster: pliable mixture of lime, sand, cement, etc. that solidifies when it dries and can be used to form walls, etc.

Relative humidity: the ratio of water vapour present in the air relative to the quantity of water vapour that would be present if the air were fully saturated.

Rot: a process of disintegration, or its result, as for example in damp wood.

– **White rot**: a fungal process causing damp wood to disintegrate and to turn white, or the result of this process.

– **Brown rot**: a fungal process causing damp wood to disintegrate and to turn brown, or the result of this process.

– **Dry rot**: a form of brown rot that takes place under conditions of little or no moisture.

Spore: a reproductive cell or "seed" of many plants and micro-organisms.

Sump: a pit or well used for collecting drainage water from a subdrain or a foundation drain and from which water is ejected by a sump pump.

Vapour barrier: A sheet of plastic installed behind drywall, intended to protect it from moisture inside the wall.

Weeping tile: perforated pipes installed below the surface of the ground around the foundation of a building to collect rainwater and drain it away from the building.

INTRODUCTION

INTRODUCTION

Since biblical times, indoor mold growth has been thought to affect the health of those living in a moldy dwelling. Today we are increasingly aware of the link between our environment and our health and well-being. Working with the provinces and territories, Health Canada first provided guidelines stating the need to minimize exposure to fungi and molds in residences in 1987. More specific guidelines for the non-industrial workplace were published in 1993, 1995 and, most recently, in 2004. The purpose of this guide is to help homeowners to respond to advice from Health Canada and other health departments in Canada to prevent and, if detected, remove mold growth indoors. It describes a process for dealing with mold in houses and provides detailed guidance both on how to eliminate indoor mold safely and on how to prevent the conditions that allow it to grow.

MOLDS—WHAT THEY ARE AND WHAT MAKES THEM GROW

Molds are microscopic organisms known as fungi, which also include yeasts and mushrooms. Together with soil bacteria, fungi play an important role in nature. By degrading plant and animal debris, they recycle waste materials, keeping the volume of waste under control. The ability of fungi to digest various materials also forms the basis of their use in food processing and in the pharmaceutical industry.

It is estimated that there are over a million species of fungi, some of which are known by the colloquial term "mold." They reproduce through spores. The fungi that grow on building materials and contents come from the soil outside. Spores come indoors mainly on soil particles tracked or blown in on soil particles in the air. This is normal and poses no hazard. However, if something becomes moldy, it can release large numbers of spores into the air. It is the spores and the by-products they produce inside homes that can be of concern to some of the occupants.

The spores of different fungi can germinate and grow on the building material closest to the natural substrate (preferred food) of the fungi involved when the moisture content is sufficient. Water is the limiting factor. If we keep things dry, molds cannot grow.

Common building materials that can be colonized by mold include drywall, wood and wood products, ceiling tiles, wallpaper and carpets. In Canadian homes, basements, crawl spaces, bathrooms and cold exterior walls are where most mold growth appears to occur, from a mixture of causes. Mold growth leads to staining and discoloration. Over time, materials can be ruined. Moldy paper and cardboard can eventually disintegrate. Fabrics can be damaged. Fungi can cause wood rot and structural damage. Growth of mold is often accompanied by musty or earthy odours which are due to by-products produced by molds.

Continued mold growth is indicative of excessive moisture conditions. The body of evidence from studies conducted in different countries relates dampness in homes to upper respiratory symptoms, but not all occupants may be affected. It is important to correct or prevent mold contamination in our homes.

Mold biology and mycology are complex subjects and the detailed discussion of them exceeds the scope of this guide. For those interested, additional information is provided in Appendix A and reference resources can be found in Appendices D and E.

HEALTH ISSUES

The Health Canada document *Fungal Contamination in Public Buildings:Health Effects and Investigation Methods* (2004) describes the health affects of indoor exposure to mold that are known today.

People respond in different ways, depending on the degree of exposure and the individual's susceptibility. People who may be at greater risk from exposure to molds include:

- infants and children;

- the elderly;

- those with respiratory conditions or allergies and asthma; and

- persons with weakened immune systems.

It is not possible to determine safe or unsafe levels of exposure to mold.

YOUR HEALTH AND YOUR HOME

If you experience persistent health problems that you think are related to exposure to molds in your home, consult your primary care physician.

Conducting a preliminary assessment of your home for indoor air quality problems may help you determine your situation (see Checklist A, p. 12). You may need to engage a professional to determine the causes of the problems and the steps to take to solve them.

HOW TO USE THIS GUIDE

This guide includes advice on how to identify and correct mold problems. By following the steps in this guide, people with little or no experience should be able to identify and correct many straightforward problems that can lead to mold growth and clean up small-scale mold contamination. This guide is not suitable to use for correcting large-scale mold problems.

Some of the information and resources presented here will also be useful for contractors and other professionals who deal with identifying and cleaning up mold problems in other kinds of buildings, such as high-rises, industrial buildings and schools. But contractors should use guidance on effective mold remediation practices for these types of buildings, such as guidelines published by the Canadian Construction Association (see www.cca-acc.com).

To use this guide safely and effectively, it is important to follow all steps in sequence. This action will ensure that the investigation and cleanup neither make the mold contamination worse nor endanger the occupants. This self-guided assessment is not intended to replace an investigation by a qualified professional. CMHC may be able to assist you in locating an indoor air-quality investigator in your area if you need help. (Call CMHC toll-free at 1 800 668-2642.)

PART I
DEFINING THE PROBLEM

Photomicrograph of spores of *Penicillium spinulosum*

PART I—DEFINING THE PROBLEM

This part consists of two steps. The accompanying checklists are designed to allow you to itemize the mold-related problems in your house. To define your mold problem, complete the following:

Step 1A) Determine if mold should be suspected (see Checklist A, p. 12)

Step 1B) Evaluate moisture problems and mold growth in your house (see Checklist B, p. 21).

Once you have completed these checklists, go to PART II—EVALUATING THE PROBLEM, in which you will use the information you have collected to determine the safest and best course of action to take to eliminate the mold damage and solve the problem.

CHECKLIST A—DETERMINE IF MOLD SHOULD BE SUSPECTED

If you can answer NO to all of these questions, you probably do not have a mold problem.

1) Does anyone in your home have symptoms that you believe are related to your home environment and which decrease in any of the following situations?

   a) Outdoors?

   b) In other peoples' homes?

   c) On holiday?

2) If your house has a basement or crawl space:

   a) Is it damp?

   b) Does it have an earth (soil) floor?

   c) Have you noticed if items stored in the basement or crawl space are stained, discoloured or covered with a fuzzy growth or smell musty?

3) Does your house have a history of any of the following:

   a) Flooding or water leaks?

   b) Plumbing leaks?

   c) Leaking roof, walls or windows?

4) Are any areas of your house excessively cold or drafty during winter?

5) Does condensation form on your walls or windows in the winter?

6) Have you noticed water stains, discoloration or mold on non-bathroom surfaces?

7) Have you or others who do not live with you noticed a musty or earthy smell:

   a) Upon entering your house?

   b) In the basement or crawl space?

EVALUATING MOISTURE PROBLEMS AND MOLD GROWTH IN YOUR HOUSE

It is now time for you to assess the extent of dampness and fungal growth in your house and decide on a reasonable course of action based on the amount of mold growth that is visible. Without exception, mold problems in houses are always associated with superfluous moisture, in effect, water damage. Such water damage may occur in different forms, such as leakage from a pipe or through a wall, or condensation of moisture on cool surfaces. Identifying moisture problems in your home is a critical step toward understanding mold problems and finding practical solutions. You may already have an idea of where the damp and moldy areas are. You will need to inspect your house from top to bottom, inside and out, and identify areas that are wet or damp, those that show signs of mold growth, and those areas that smell musty or earthy. Appendix B of this document provides more detailed information on what to look for and will be helpful if you want to conduct a more complete investigation.

What to look for

The goals of this investigation are twofold:

1) To find moisture problems

2) To locate, measure and tally the amount of surface area affected by mold growth

Although molds require moisture to grow, they do not need much. Your investigation will accordingly have to consider all degrees of moisture damage, ranging from sopping wet to slightly damp. Materials that are saturated with water are easy to spot. More problematic are those areas that look and feel dry but were wet and moldy from a past event, and those that are only slightly damp yet sufficiently so that they may be a breeding ground for mold. Several techniques are available to help you detect these less obvious problems.

We recommend that people who are either very sensitive or ill, and who are unable to enlist a friend or family member to carry out the investigation for them, take precautions against exposure as described in Part III of this guide (see "Protecting yourself," p. 33).

Water and wetness

Throughout your investigation, be conscious of the effects of gravity on the movement of water. The lowest part of any material subject to a leak is likely to be the wettest, which is especially true of walls. If you locate a leak, carefully trace the routes that the water has traveled. Floor drains in basements are intentionally installed at the lowest points in the floor. The area around these drains is a good place to look for the tiny dried riverbeds leftover from previous flooding (more about floor drains later). Similarly, dry drip marks may remain after condensed moisture has dripped down the interior side of cold exterior walls in winter. Whatever the point of entry or source of the water, its path then becomes a downward one, always moving toward the lowest point. Free water, as described above, is frequently the cause of indoor mold growth.

However, many molds are highly efficient scavengers for moisture and are able to grow on materials that are nowhere close to being saturated.

The importance of humidity

Warm air has a greater capacity to contain moisture than cool air. When warm, moisture-laden air comes into contact with a cooler surface, the air itself becomes cooled. If the air is cooled enough, it may become unable to retain its moisture content, which then collects on the surface as tiny droplets of liquid water called **condensation**. This process is the same that causes dew to form. The **dew point** is the temperature at which air is cool enough to produce condensation. This temperature varies according to the moisture content of the air. **Relative humidity** defines the ratio of water vapour present in the air, relative to the quantity of water vapour that would be present if the air were fully saturated. We see the practical consequences of relative humidity and dew point every day in our own homes, when we climb out of a hot shower and encounter a steamy mirror. But relative humidity is also important in causing moisture to accumulate in places other than the bathroom. Here are three common scenarios whereby excess moisture in the air may lead to moisture problems and mold growth within your home:

1) Condensation may form on the interior side of poorly insulated exterior walls or windows during the winter. Many different molds like to grow on damp painted or papered wall surfaces, as well as wooden windowsills. (Winter problem.)

2) Uninsulated cold water pipes may drip condensation, causing local moisture damage. This happens most commonly along the incoming water line in the basement. Items that lie beneath these drips may get wet and grow moldy. (Summer problem.)

3) Porous organic materials, such as textiles, paper, cardboard and leather, have a tendency to absorb airborne moisture. When stored under conditions of high relative humidity, such as in a damp basement, these items may soon become moldy. (Basement or garage problem.)

Condensation on window

As part of your structural investigation, consider measuring the relative humidity in all the places that you inspect. To do this you will need a relative-humidity meter, also known as a hygrometer. You can purchase a hygrometer fairly inexpensively at a hardware store. Ideally, the indoor relative humidity during the heating season should be low enough to prevent condensation on the windows. Relative humidities of 25 to 35 per cent are not unusual. The suggested upper limit is 45 per cent during the winter. Dust mite problems are less likely when the relative humidity is kept below 50 per cent. The detailed moisture investigation discussed in Appendix B lists several tips for reducing indoor relative humidity.

Signs, symptoms and tests for moisture

Staining is the most common feature associated with water damage. It is most often seen on wood and paper products that have become saturated with water, causing some of the natural colouring of these materials to migrate to the edges of the area that is or has been wet, much like the darkened ring encircling a coffee stain. This sort of staining is more obvious on light-coloured materials, especially those items that contain unbleached fibre, such as wood, cardboard and ceiling tiles. Another common feature of dampness is a general darkening in colour of materials following the absorption of water. As you proceed through the steps of this investigation, look at all the materials in good lighting and judge their colour. Items that appear darker than they should be may be damp even though they may not feel so to the touch.

Sticky tape test—You can sometimes test items for dampness by affixing a small strip of plastic tape. The tape is less likely to stick if there is dampness in the material. (Be sure to test this method on a sample of the same material that you know to be dry, to ensure that the failure of the tape to stick is not due to something other than dampness.)

Plastic patch test—Another way to test for dampness on walls or floors is by affixing a piece of clear, medium-weight plastic (1 m²– 11 sq. ft.– or less) directly against the material. Seal it on all four sides with duct tape. Leave the plastic on overnight or longer, then remove the patch and check it for signs of condensation on the plastic, which indicates the presence of moisture in the underlying material. The limitations of this test are that the moisture may be released at a very slow rate (you need a long observation period) or only during certain times of the year.

Moisture meter testing—The most sophisticated test for dampness is an instrument known as a moisture meter. A moisture meter is used in the construction industry to test the moisture content of building materials such as wood, drywall and concrete, to know when they are dry enough to be painted or finished. One kind of moisture meter has two tiny pins that are pushed into the material to be tested. Because a temperature correction must be applied to the meter reading, use of a moisture meter is best left to the professional.

How can I tell if it is mold?

Discoloration can be a sign of mold, although it is not always due to mold. Light-coloured carpeting near baseboards, for example, can become stained by outdoor pollution entering the home through air leakage. Similarly, combustion products produced inside the house—from cigarette smoke and the burning of candles or incense—can cause the carpet to darken at the perimeter. When mold grows on a surface, it is usually conspicuous. Surfaces that appear to the naked eye to be free of mold in most cases are. Mold growth usually looks fuzzy or powdery, and is very often coloured, from light green to brown or black.

Paper swipe test—With a small strip of coarse paper (a coffee filter works well), gently rub the surface of the suspected mold colony. If powdery residue rubs off onto the paper, it is possible that the material you sampled was mold. This test works especially well with dark-coloured molds. Interpret this test cautiously, however, because some substances that are not molds will rub off on paper (for example, soot).

Bleach test—A reasonably reliable test is to dab the stain or mark with undiluted chlorine laundry bleach and observe any changes in colour. If the colour is entirely or largely removed after one to two hours, then the stain is likely organic and may be mold. Otherwise, the stain or mark is probably inorganic and likely not mold.

Flashlight test—In a darkened room, hold your flashlight against the surface suspected of harbouring mold colonies so that the beam shines across or is parallel to the surface. Any irregularities of the surface, such as mold growth, will be accentuated by their shadow and appear as fine fuzz. This test works well with light-coloured molds that may not be readily visible when viewed in direct light.

Organic versus inorganic materials

Mold growth is usually worst on materials of organic origin—materials that are made of plant or animal products such as paper, cardboard, wood, canvas, leather and wool as well as non-biological hydrocarbons, such as vinyl and plastic. Materials such as metal, concrete, stone and glass are inorganic, although when these materials are painted or have accumulated dirt, their surfaces effectively become organic. Although inorganic materials are much more resistant to mold growth than organic ones, you should inspect everything just to be sure.

Questions to ask

To reiterate, dampness and mold growth go together. It is essential to have a clear picture of the magnitude of fungal growth to know how to proceed properly with cleaning, because the health hazards posed by mold contamination are proportional to the size of the surface affected. Keep the following questions in mind as you proceed:

- Are there signs and symptoms of moisture damage?
- Was the area subjected to flooding or a wetting event?
- Is there visible water leakage?
- Is there standing water, such as a basement sump or a sink with a dripping faucet?
- Does water condense on windows or walls during the winter?
- Is water condensing on cold water pipes in the basement?
- Is the relative humidity high?
- Is there obvious staining or mold growth on surfaces?
- How large are the areas affected?
- Are there musty odours?

Keep in mind that things you might consider to be a normal part of your day-to-day life may contribute unacceptably high levels of moisture to the home environment. Each person contributes a total of between two and seven litres to the indoor air daily. This includes water generated by activities such as cooking, washing/drying clothes and showering/bathing. Among other indoor things that can generate moisture are aquarium tanks, potted plants, hot tubs and saunas. In addition to leaks and condensation, take note of these normal moisture-generating activities as you conduct your investigation.

What you will need

The following simple tools will help you to access all the elements of your house; help you to see in dark or awkward places; allow you to poke and prod the various elements of construction; and help you to measure conditions around you.

- Flashlight
- Bottle of standard laundry bleach
- Humidity tester [optional]
- Measuring tape
- Moisture meter [optional]
- Notepad, paper and pencil or pen
- Personal protective equipment (see Appendix F)
- Roll of clear plastic tape
- Roll of duct tape
- Standard (flat) screwdriver
- Several sturdy, clear plastic bags, such as freezer bags.

CONDUCTING YOUR INVESTIGATION

Proceed systematically through the house, first outside from top to bottom, and then inside from bottom to top. Investigate your house thoroughly using Checklist B, page 21, as your guide. Don't be afraid to conduct your survey in the rain, since you might then notice problems that would otherwise be missed.

Starting outside, note any of the following deficiencies:

Downspout on house

- Missing or lifting shingles, damaged siding

- Chipped or cracked brickwork or foundations

- Leaky or clogged eavestroughs

- No downspout or extension missing (see photo)

- Water pooling against the foundation, soggy soil, moss, etc.

When you have finished checking the exterior, go inside.
This time start at the basement and work your way up. Try to organize your investigation by zones, completing one zone before proceeding to the next. Take note of:

- Constantly wet areas, such as a wall or floor next to a water tank, sump pit or leaky pipe.

- Occasionally wet areas. (Some houses have a "stream" during the spring or have running water after a heavy rain.)

- Surfaces damp to the touch, darker in colour, or identified as damp using the tests described above.

- Basement or crawl space floor of exposed soil or gravel.

- Water staining.

- Mold-like discolorations.

- Mushroom-like growths.

- Rotting, crumbling or powdery wood.

- Areas with musty, earthy or sour odours, or other unusual smells.

- White powdery accumulations on cement, brick or plaster
  (see ***Efflorescence*** in "Glossary" or Appendix B, page 60).

Visible moisture and mold

With a measuring tape, roughly measure the dimensions of the mold-colonized surfaces. If you don't have a measuring tape, estimate the area. Write down the size of the affected areas on the last page of **Checklist B**, page 21. When you have completed a zone, tally the total surface area affected by mold growth (in the metric system, each square metre contains 10,000 square centimetres, and in the imperial system, each square foot of area contains 144 square inches). For your information, note down the colour or other characteristics of the mold growth. However, this information is not necessary for determining cleaning procedures.

Do not disrupt any potentially contaminated materials at this stage. Note the presence of obvious mold growth and measure or estimate the affected surface area. Test all solid-surface materials in damp locations with the "flashlight test," page 16. If in doubt about whether some surface fuzziness is mold, confirm it using the "paper-swipe test" or the "bleach test, page 16."

Hidden mold growth

Sometimes mold-colonized materials are hidden from view, such as on the inside of wall cavities. A musty or earthy smell may indicate the presence of mold (although not all molds are accompanied by musty smells). Hidden mold growth presents a dilemma for inspectors because, while it is possible that sufficient hidden mold could negatively affect the health of occupants, there is no way to assure its absence nor determine its presence short of literally taking everything apart. Such action is, of course, usually impractical. Many inspectors use a combination of their exterior observations and their intuition to guide them in making a limited number of cuts into the enclosed spaces that they expect to represent "worst-case" areas. Their rationale is that if these areas are free from mold growth, then there is a reasonable possibility that the remaining areas are so as well. This method has its limitations. Nevertheless, it's a starting point, and a seasoned inspector often brings to an investigation an uncannily accurate intuition when it comes to finding hidden mold. Yet without this level of experience, the question remains, how can you satisfy yourself as to the absence of mold growth in hidden building elements?

Your best option is to use a similar approach to that of the seasoned inspector, but build instead on your own experience and knowledge of the house to provide you with clues as to where to look. After you have carried out a moisture investigation, you will have identified areas of moisture leaks, condensation and seepage. Try to envision how the water got to the places where you found it. If that path took it through the wall, then there is a strong possibility of mold damage within the wall cavity in that area. On the other hand, if the problem is primarily condensation-related (such as poorly insulated walls that are relatively air/vapour-tight), it is possible that air that gets inside the walls may be relatively dry, the moisture having first condensed on the room side of the wall. Only consider invasive checking methods (i.e., cutting into walls) as a last resort, to be used especially where your walls are of drywall construction and you strongly suspect water penetration from the exterior. Normally, invasive checking is conducted as part of the repair process rather than during the investigation, as it requires much of the same equipment and construction skill as the repair itself. Common sense and a bit of detective work can go a long way to help you identify hidden mold growth sites.

Heating and ventilation systems

Mold growth in heating and ventilation systems is a particular concern because of its greater potential to become airborne, exposing occupants to mold spores and other materials. Mold growth in heating systems or ductwork is usually the result of moisture from one of the following three sources:

- Water leakage onto or into ducts

- Malfunctioning or inadequate maintenance of a built-in humidifier

- Excessive use of cooling in the summer, leading to internal condensation.

If you suspect that mold is growing on the inside of any part of your heating and ventilation system, have it examined by an expert prior to attempting any clean-up. Attempting to clean these systems yourself risks making the problem worse and exposing the occupants to moldy materials.

Unaffected areas and items

Some articles are not themselves affected by moisture damage or mold growth, yet they may have been present in an area where mold growth has been found and may harbour on their surfaces accumulated mold spores. Unless the indoor mold levels have been extremely high, surface contamination of solid indoor furnishings or surfaces like tables, appliances and picture frames is not a hazard; it can be removed by ordinary cleaning practices. The same holds true for plush furniture, such as sofas and rugs. Nevertheless, these items tend to absorb musty odours and dust is harder to clean from their surfaces.

Summary

- Proceed systematically through the house

- Use the above descriptions to help you interpret what you see

- Keep track, on **Checklist B**, of the areas exhibiting moisture damage and mold growth

Please note that this preliminary investigation does not replace the services of a trained indoor-air quality investigator. We strongly suggest that you **consult with a professional investigator before you undertake costly renovations intended to solve indoor environmental problems.**

CHECKLIST B—HOMEOWNER'S MOISTURE AND MOLD INVESTIGATION

Location	Description of problem	Estimated mold-affected surface (m²/sq.ft.)
Exterior of house		
Roof		
Eaves, eavestroughs downspouts		
Chimney		
Flashings		
Cladding/siding		
Windows		
Foundation walls		
Grading/drainage		
Interior of house		
Basement — Unfinished interior sides of exterior walls		
Finished interior sides of exterior walls		
Basement Floor — Carpeting		
Other		
Structural Wood		
Finished wood surfaces		
Sump		
Suspected hidden damage		

Location		Description of problem	Estimated mold-affected surface (m²/sq.ft.)
Furnishings and stored items	Living space		
	Laundry area		
	Hobby areas		
	Stored items		
Mechanical Systems	Heating systems		
	Humidification /dehumidification		
	Plumbing		
Exhaust ventilation	Clothes dryer		
	Range hoods		
	Bathroom fans		

Upper floors

Location	Description of problem	Estimated mold-affected surface (m²/sq.ft.)
Interior sides of exterior walls		
Interior walls		
Suspected hidden damage		
Carpets-rugs		
Windows— windowsills		
Ceilings		
Heating systems		
Plumbing		

Location		Description of problem	Estimated mold-affected surface (m²/sq.ft.)
Attic	Air leakage (see Appendix B)		
	Insulation		
	Roof deck		
	Roof leaks		
	Ventilation (see Appendix B)		

Location	Description of problem	Estimated mold-affected surface (m²/sq.ft.)
Aquarium tanks		
House plants		
Other		

Other Sources

Total surface area affected by mold (m² or sq. ft.)

Occupancy

What is the approximate floor area of the living space in your house (m² or sq. ft.)?	How many people live in your house?

Notes

_____

_____

_____

_____

_____

PART II
EVALUATING THE PROBLEM

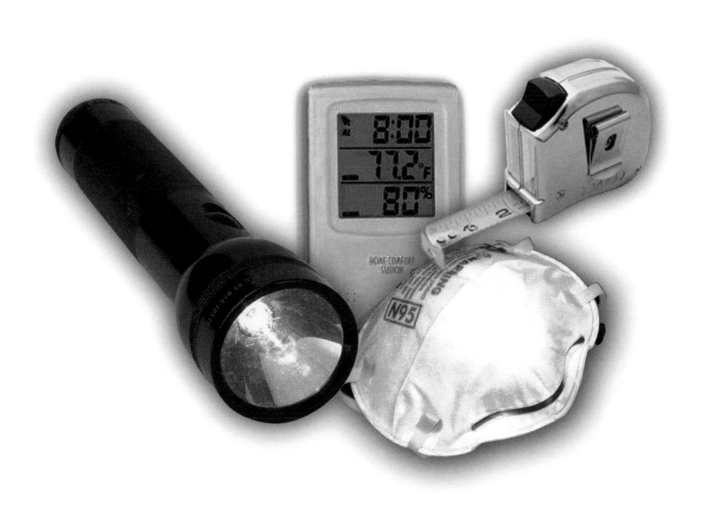

PART II—EVALUATING THE PROBLEM

This section is designed to help you determine how to approach solving a mold problem in your house. To use the Decision Chart below, move across to the right until you reach the column that best describes your findings on **Checklist B**—Homeowners' Moisture and Mold Investigation.

DECISION CHART	**Total Surface Area Affected By Mold* (from CHECKLIST B)**			
	I or more patches, one of which is greater than 3 m² (30 sq. ft.)	I or more separated patches, each smaller than 3 m² (30 sq. ft.)	More than 3 patches, each smaller than I m² (I0 sq. ft.)	3 or fewer patches, each smaller than I m² (I0 sq. ft.)
	Expert assessment and cleanup required	**Expert assessment recommended, but homeowners may attempt cleanup using proper precautions**		**Homeowner can attempt cleanup using proper precautions**

* 30 sq. ft. = approx. 3 m²; 10 sq. ft. = approx. 1 m²

FINDING AN INDOOR AIR QUALITY INVESTIGATOR

You may need professional assistance when:

- There is a lot of mold.

- The home is very damp.

- Mold comes back even after repeated cleaning.

- An occupant is experiencing health problems and suspects they are mold related.

Contact your local CMHC office or call toll free at 1 800 668-2642 for a list of persons in your area who have completed the CMHC Residential Indoor Air Quality (IAQ) Investigator Program. Ask for a copy of *Breathe Healthier Air in Your Home—A Consumer Guide to Residential Indoor Air Quality Investigations.* Trained IAQ investigators are independent business operators who specialize in providing home consultations based on your concerns. They will provide you with a written report outlining the IAQ problems in your house and will recommend strategies to improve the overall indoor air quality in your house. Note that home inspections conducted for real estate transactions are primarily to document the conditions and deficiencies of the home at the time of the inspection and generally do not consider indoor air quality problems.

HIRING A MOLD REMEDIATION CONTRACTOR

Your best sources for finding out about reliable contractors are referrals from family and friends, or hardware and building supply stores.

Ask the contractor what kind of training he or she has taken. Inquire about the procedures the contractor follows to clean mold and how the contractor would ensure that the mold contamination is contained. What protective measures does he or she employ?

You want to find a contractor who has a good understanding of mold and the need to protect your family, prevent the mold from spreading to the rest of the house and also to protect the people who will be working. The level of care should be appropriate to the work. Applying much more than necessary, for example; complex equipment, full suits or powered respirators for a moderate area of mold, may end up costing you more.

More information on selecting contractors can be found in the CMHC publications *Before You Renovate,* order number 61001, and *Healthy Housing Renovation Planner,* order number 60957.

PART III
FIXING THE PROBLEM

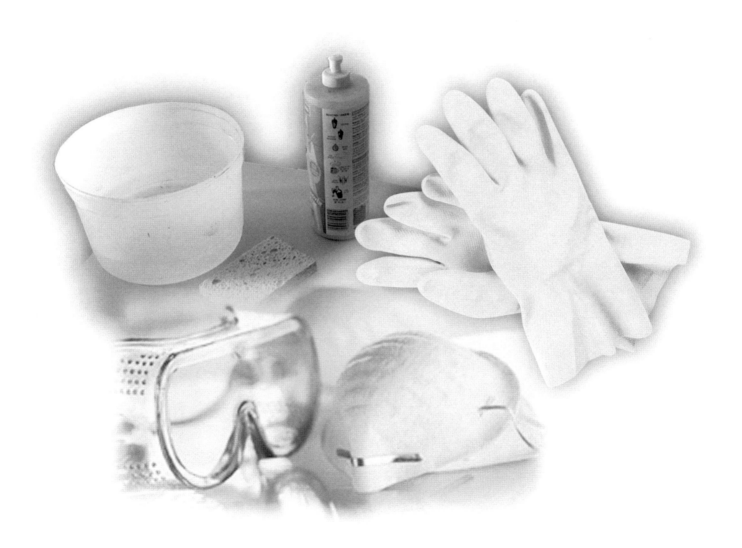

PART III—FIXING THE PROBLEM

Most mold problems can be prevented by keeping all surfaces as clean and dry as possible and not allowing indoor air to become too moist. Once problems occur, however, we need to take more aggressive measures. This section deals with how to fix mold problems. The three steps in any mold cleanup include understanding the key principles, getting rid of the mold and completing the cleanup.

UNDERSTANDING KEY PRINCIPLES

Removing the mold

The first goal in fixing the problem is to remove contaminated materials in such a way that we prevent contaminated dust from spreading from the contaminated area. Discard or decontaminate anything that has been wet, or even subject to long periods of dampness (such as in a wet basement or crawl space.) This action may seem excessive, but it is often the least expensive and least time-consuming step; it is also the best move for your health. If an item cannot be washed or dry-cleaned, you may have no other way to solve the problem. This may be a good time to discard unneeded items. Items that are causing health problems are a liability, not an asset. If your discards are going to be recycled, please advise future owners about the mold contamination and the risks that may be associated with using (or even storing) these items if they are not effectively decontaminated.

Cleaning up the residue

The second goal is to clean and decontaminate washable and dry-cleanable items and surfaces, using this document as a guide. You can clean non-moldy surfaces and materials with unscented soap or detergent and water. Scrub or sponge with a rag and rinse well. Be sure to dry them quickly and ventilate well, unless it is humid outside.
If it is humid, wait for a drier spell before you start extensive wet-washing. Wash clothes and other fabrics and dry them quickly. Dry-clean those that cannot be washed.

The recommended cleaning process for eliminating indoor mold has correctly been called an extreme form of spring cleaning. **The best cleanser for cleaning mold-contaminated surfaces is simple warm water and unscented detergent.** When a heavy-duty grease remover is needed, use a solution of trisodium phosphate (TSP) in warm water. TSP is available at hardware stores and paint stores. Since TSP is caustic, you must use gloves and eye protection.

Avoid using bleach and other chemical disinfectants. Disinfectants like bleach do not prevent mold problems from recurring and these chemicals should be used with caution because many are quite toxic.

Fixing the moisture problem

The third goal, after cleaning up the residue, is to eliminate the moisture problem that allowed the mold to grow in the first place. Even rigorous cleaning will not prevent future problems unless you eliminate the underlying cause of the mold growth. The source of excessive moisture that creates a growth environment for molds must be found and fixed (see Appendix C, "Preventing moisture problems," page 80.)

In summary, to eliminate an indoor mold problem and prevent re-growth, you must carry out several steps. The following measures can help to improve any housing unit and make it more sanitary for the residents:

- discard or clean any materials that show mold growth or are located near a growth site

- find and eliminate sources of superfluous moisture

- reduce clutter and keep surfaces dry and clean

- provide continuous, controlled ventilation and dehumidification if necessary

To test or not to test

Some people are concerned that mold should be tested before it is cleaned up. Testing generally involves taking a small sample of the mold, usually as an impression on Scotch tape, and submitting it to a laboratory for identification or confirmation. In most cases, the added expense of testing mold is not warranted if the scale of contamination involves less than 3 m^2 (30 sq. ft.), because the clean-up procedures you would use would not be influenced by laboratory results. Appendix F, page 89 discusses the pros and cons of mold testing in greater detail and provides information on testing laboratories and other services.

GETTING RID OF THE MOLD

The following sections are designed to help you clean up the mold problem. Before you begin, it is very important to ensure that the problem can safely be cleaned using these methods. If you have determined from the previous section (see **Part II** "Evaluating the Problem.") that the area of surface affected by mold growth is less than 3 m² (30 sq. ft.), then these methods may be used. **If adjoining mold-affected surfaces exceed 3 m² in area, obtain professional assistance: do not use the repair methods described in this section yourself.**

Protecting Yourself

While you clean up moldy debris, it is important to take care not to expose yourself or others to mold spores and contaminated dusts, because these materials may be allergenic or poisonous. To protect yourself from inhaling these materials, use the correct type of mask and ensure it is properly fitted.

Comfort Mask—This type of mask removes some large particles but is not rated for dangerous conditions. It is inexpensive, disposable, and fairly easy to put on, but it seldom fits well. There are many examples, including the 3M #8500 comfort mask. Use this mask only for low-concern conditions and change it for a new mask every few hours.

N95 Dust Respirator—This type of respirator is available at most safety supply outlets and home improvement stores. It can be used to exclude fine dust when the risk is considered to be low. It is inexpensive, disposable, and designed to reduce risk by a 10:1 ratio. Dispose of it after use to minimize your risk of contamination inside the facepiece. An example is the 3M Dust N95 #8210 respirator.

Half-face or Full-Face Elastomeric Respirators—These respirators consist of a half-facepiece (to be used with safety goggles) or full-facepiece with either one or a pair of disposable filters. Depending on the type of filter used, these respirators protect against particulates, vapours, gases or a combination of these contaminants. Particulate filters are divided into three types: N (Non-Oil), R (Oil-Resistant) and P (Oil-Proof). If properly fitted, they can reduce your risk by 100:1. Use this type of respirator, 3M #6000 full-facepiece and 3M #2091 P100 filter or equivalent, where conditions cause high concern.

Note that a good fit is essential with all tight-fitting respirators, which is normally not possible for people with beards. These respirators will not provide good protection if poorly fitted; take care to avoid leakage. Replace the respirator if the facepiece is cracked, extremely soft or damaged. Replace the filters when you feel resistance to breathing or when they look dirty.

Anyone considering spending a significant length of time cleaning mold should buy and follow the recommendations in CSA Z94.4, *Selection, Use and Care of Respirators*, available from Canadian Standards Association offices. That document as well as the manufacturer's instructions discuss considerations of fit.

Skin and eye protection—Just as mold can cause lung irritation and allergies, skin contact with mold and materials on which mold has grown can sometimes result in rashes and irritation. During mold cleanup, the risk of skin contact with mold is great. Skin reactions can be prevented easily by wearing gloves during clean-up procedures. Ordinary work gloves offer good protection against abrasions and blisters during manual work, but they do not provide an adequate barrier against moldy materials. When dealing with mold, always wear disposable latex or nitrile gloves and cover them with a second pair of standard work gloves for heavy work.

Any work that may generate airborne dust or debris has the potential to injure your eyes. Always wear safety glasses or goggles during this work as a precautionary measure.

Protecting Others

Even if you follow all the precautions outlined in this guide, your cleanup may still inadvertently disrupt and release into the air some mold spores. This release is not normally a concern for other healthy occupants of your residence. As a precaution during cleanup, however, it is a good idea for babies, the elderly and sensitive persons, such as those with allergies, asthma or weakened immune systems (for example, by diabetes or HIV) or people undergoing cancer treatment or receiving treatment for an organ transplant to leave the house. If you are in doubt about which people in your home may be sensitive to mold exposure, consult your physician.

Minimize the amount of dust generated by working slowly and avoiding sudden movements. Apply a light mist of clean water to materials that you intend to remove but do not drench them. It may help to add a drop or two of liquid dishwashing detergent per gallon of misting water. This helps the water to soak in and stops it from beading on the surface.

Isolating the Area

Before beginning your cleanup, isolate the work area to prevent the escape of mold spores into other areas of the house. You can do this in the following ways:

- close doors to adjoining, non-work areas

- shut off the blower on a forced-air furnace and temporarily seal off the vents

- drape plastic sheeting as a barrier across doorways lacking doors

- install a fan in a window and depressurize the work area.

Cleaning Techniques

As you prepare to start cleaning, you may wonder about the merits of different commercially available cleaning products, some of which also function as disinfectants. The main objective of cleaning is to remove unwanted material, typically dirt or grime, from a material or surface by scrubbing with water containing either a detergent (which makes dirt more soluble) or a wetting agent, such as soap. Commercial cleaning products mostly differ in the compounds they contain for these purposes and many contain perfumes or deodorizers or both. We recommend that you use unscented detergents or soaps to help you determine if you have successfully removed musty odours.

Pros and cons of disinfection

Cleaning removes most dirt and grime, improves appearances and makes things more sanitary. In some situations, however, even trace amounts of the contaminant can cause harm. In hospitals, for example, surgical instruments and other items may become contaminated by infectious microbes (germs) after contact with patients. These items need a special kind of follow-up cleaning called "disinfection" in which they are treated with chemicals such as disinfectants, germicides and biocides (like bleach). Disinfection kills microbes that remain on surfaces, thus preventing their transfer from patient to patient. However, disinfection is only meaningful when the contaminant is also an infectious substance, such that cleaning alone could not prevent the risk of infection.

Note that no commonly-occurring indoor fungi are known to cause human infection. Furthermore, disinfection does not prevent mold problems from returning. The only way to prevent mold problems is to eliminate excess moisture.

Porous, semi-porous and non-porous materials

The extent to which wet-cleaning methods can be effective depends on the porousness (or porosity) of the surface. Non-porous materials like glass, metal and plastic are smooth and do not absorb cleaning solutions. These materials are usually the easiest to clean. Semi-porous materials like concrete and wood tend to absorb small amounts of cleaning solutions, making thorough removal of dirt more difficult. Porous materials like paper, fabrics, carpets and insulation are the most difficult of all to clean because they are very absorbent. Only a few such materials can successfully be cleaned using wet processes (for example, laundry). To clean non-launderable, porous items effectively, homeowners can use a vacuum cleaner with a **HEPA filter** (see next section).

Vacuum Cleaning

Vacuum cleaners can be useful in removing mold, dust and debris. They can also, however, accidentally increase your exposure to these materials. The very action of disturbing a carpet can re-suspend fine particles such as spores. Thus, it is suggested that an N95 respirator is worn while vacuuming. Similarly, ordinary vacuum cleaners do not trap very fine particles effectively. Because of this, mold spores and other fine particles may be blown out through the exhaust of the vacuum cleaner and back into the room air.

Central vacuum cleaning systems that exhaust directly to the outdoors solve this problem of blowing dust back into the room and thus are much better at preventing contamination of the indoor air by airborne spores. Special vacuum cleaners that use High-Efficiency Particulate Air (**HEPA**) filters to trap fine particles also improve safety. A professional cleaner with a truck-mounted vacuum system can also be a safe alternative because only the hose and attachments are brought indoors. Even with these methods, use deliberate, careful sweeps to avoid stirring up fine dirt.

Ordinary vacuum cleaners

Do not use an ordinary vacuum cleaner for mold cleanup! Ordinary vacuum cleaners, even expensive and powerful ones, can make mold problems far worse by increasing the level of airborne spores.

HEPA vacuum cleaners

You can obtain special vacuum cleaners with **HEPA filters** on the exhaust flow that are acceptable for mold cleanup if they are used in conjunction with the techniques described below. **HEPA filters**, like those used on breathing masks, are designed to trap very fine particles, including mold spores. Vacuum cleaners equipped with **HEPA filters** are more expensive than regular portable vacuum cleaners, but they are the only kind of portable vacuum cleaner that should ever be used for cleaning mold-contaminated surfaces.

Central vacuum cleaners

Central vacuum cleaners exhausted directly to the outdoors can be used successfully to clean mold if the exhaust line from the vacuum cleaner is completely airtight. Bear in mind that the exhaust vent should be mounted outside the house, preferably located on the leeward side of the house (opposite to the side against which the wind usually blows) so that dust will be carried away from the house and not be blown back through cracks, open doors or windows when the wind blows. Central vacuum cleaners that exhaust indoors to the basement or the garage should never be used for cleaning mold.

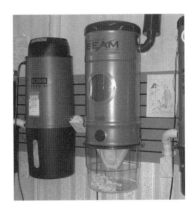

Testing your vacuum cleaner

Regardless of the filtration, make sure that whatever vacuum cleaner you use has sufficient suction to draw in any spores or other dust that are generated during cleaning, especially if your vacuum cleaner has a beater bar. To test whether your vacuum cleaner is adequate for mold cleanup, you first need to find a carpet that you are sure is mold-free in a room that you can make completely dark. This test may be easiest to do at night. Before you start the vacuum, switch off all the lights and shine your flashlight around the room. If dust is suspended in the air, you will be able to see it in the beam of the flashlight. If the air is relatively free of dust, then vacuum clean the room. Then, do the flashlight test again. If you can see dust in the flashlight beam, then your vacuum cleaner isn't working properly and isn't suitable for your cleanup.

Recommended vacuum-cleaning technique (for carpeted floors)

Practise the following techniques regardless of the type of vacuum cleaner used. The recommended way of vacuuming surfaces involves these steps:

- Carefully stroke the object being cleaned with the cleaner head, in a forward direction only, then slightly lift during the return stroke to capture local dust in the air.

- Stroke from all four directions if possible, but at least two directions at right angles to each other.

- Clean for a minimum of two minutes for each square metre, much more than for normal cleaning.

- Avoid using beater-bar heads unless they are designed to avoid releasing clouds of particles that cannot be captured by the suction.

Professional cleaners

Professional cleaning services that use a truck-mounted vacuum system can protect you from fine dust if the operators are careful not to stir up dust while they clean. Most companies, however, are not aware of the need to avoid aggressive cleaning techniques. They should use extra time and care, and refrain from rubbing or beating vigorously. The same precautions that you should take in hiring contractors also apply to cleaners.

Disposal of Moldy Items

You will certainly encounter items or materials that cannot be cleaned and will require disposal. Considerations on disposal and reuse are described below, according to the material in question. However, as a rule, there are no legal restrictions on the disposal of mold-contaminated materials (at least this is true at the time of writing of this guide). To be safe, check with your local waste disposal authorities to ensure that no local bylaws require specific disposal methods.

Do not recycle mold-contaminated items. Be aware that you may be held personally liable if the new owner experiences health problems arising from the reuse of your moldy items. Anyone who considers reusing such items should do so at his own risk and should be properly informed of the history of the items and the possible hazards associated with their use.

Cleaning moldy items is a laborious task. Take this opportunity to discard stored items that you do not use and no longer need. Eliminating clutter is also desirable for good air circulation.

Professional cleaners bagging mold for disposal

Responding to a Flood

Where a flood has occurred in an area that had not previously been exposed to moisture damage, you have only a limited time to clean up before molds begin to grow—usually no more than 48 hours. During this time, you can safely remove water-damaged items and construction materials without the risk of mold exposure. Acting quickly is desirable for two reasons: 1) you can save a great deal of money by doing the work yourself and not having to hire special mold clean-up contractors; and 2) you may be able to rescue items that would be destroyed by mold if left longer. You can find specific instructions on flood clean-up in a separate CMHC publication, *Cleaning Up Your House after a Flood,* order number 61094.

COMPLETING THE CLEANUP

Using the information that you collected from previous sections of this guide, establish a priority list of areas that require cleaning and repair. Focus your efforts on the worst area first and then proceed to the areas less affected. If you do not think that you can complete all of your cleaning in one session, break up your cleaning efforts so that you can complete an entire area or room before stopping.

As you proceed with your cleanup, keep in mind that some items, themselves not affected by mold growth, may have come into contact with airborne mold spores and may become hopelessly contaminated as a result. Be aware that many of the stories that clutter the Internet about people whose homes were devastated by mold and who set fire to all their belongings for fear of inadvertently contaminating their new homes with mold, involve unfortunate and dismaying over-reactions based on misinformation. **The spores of molds, including toxigenic species and those that cause damage in damp houses, are present in the air everywhere, all the time. Minor levels of residual dormant spores on furniture or building materials do not place these items at any increased risk of developing mold problems in the future, nor does their presence present a risk to human health.** To reiterate, the only way that mold growth on any item can be effectively avoided is by preventing moisture damage.

Vacuum moldy surfaces with a vacuum cleaner which has a HEPA filter or is externally exhausted as the first step to remove the bulk of the mold on the surface.

Walls and Ceilings

Drywall

On walls and ceilings made of drywall that show less than 0.1 m² (1 sq. ft.) of mold growth, cleaning using the above methods may be effective. For larger areas of mold growth, removing the affected drywall may be a more effective strategy. If you are unfamiliar with installing and repairing drywall and are not able to acquire the necessary skills, you may have no choice but to hire a contractor.

Before removing the affected areas of drywall, cover their surfaces first with plastic fixed in place with duct tape. This shield reduces the amount of dust generated. Before you cut away any drywall, make sure that the wall does not contain electrical wires that could be damaged. The best way to cut drywall is with a utility knife rather than a saw. A utility knife is easier to control and generates far less dust. Make sure that the blade is new and set the depth of the cut to the thickness of the drywall, usually half an inch. Cut in several passes, slowly and with even pressure. If you try to cut through the entire thickness all at once or too quickly, you risk slipping and injuring yourself. Once you have cut through the drywall thickness, remove the section using a pry-bar. For patching the removed sections, it helps to ensure that the section you cut out spans at least two stud or joist surfaces to which you can affix the drywall patch.

Bag the removed pieces of drywall using double garbage bags with ties, and limit the amount of material in each bag. Bags should be easy to lift and the plastic should not be under stress.

Plaster

Walls made of **plaster** and **lath** (see Appendix B, page 60) are usually a lot less susceptible to serious mold problems than those made of drywall. It is usually possible to clean these kinds of walls without having to rebuild them. Plaster wall surfaces only need to be removed in severe cases where the amount of water damage has caused the plaster to crack or fragment. Plaster walls can usually be cleaned using the cleaning techniques already described. Remember that, because it is a semi-porous material, plaster will absorb moisture applied to it. To reduce the amount of moisture absorbed, take care to use only the minimal amount of cleaning solution. Make sure that you allow the affected wall surfaces to dry completely before repainting or replacing finishes.

If you need to repaint damaged walls or ceilings, be aware that many commonly used acrylic latex paints can be susceptible to mold growth when they are applied to uninsulated walls. Mold-resistant or antimicrobial paints are not a substitute for keeping the walls clean and dry. Moreover, some people may react negatively to the antimicrobial chemicals that are used in these products. Avoid using wallpaper on walls where moisture problems are likely, such as the interior sides of exterior walls, in bathrooms and in the basement.

Insulation

We commonly see small amounts of discoloration on insulation around cracks or breaks in the **vapour barrier** (see Appendix B, page 60) such as around electrical boxes. Usually, these marks are not mold but rather are due to suspended airborne particles, like car exhaust or candle smoke, adhering to the fibres where air can move through the insulation. It is similar to the staining that commonly occurs on light-coloured carpeting along the base of the interior side of exterior walls in drafty houses.

In general, mold does not grow well on insulation materials, such as fibreglass and cellulose insulation, unless these materials remain wet to the point of saturation for at least several days or weeks. Fibreglass insulation is largely inorganic (glass), and the organic resin binding agents used in manufacturing fibreglass are of little interest to most microbes. The fire-retardant chemicals used to treat cellulose insulation protect it against mold growth, which is not the case in most other cellulose-based materials.

Professionals remove damaged insulation

The thermal insulation properties of these materials, however, are greatly diminished once they become wet and compressed. Thus, even though there may not be an obvious mold problem, always replace wet insulation.

During the removal of damp insulation, take the precautions outlined earlier. These procedures, including the use of gloves, an appropriate breathing mask, eye protection and dust minimization techniques, will help to protect you against both mold exposure and exposure to insulation fibres, which can cause significant irritation to the eyes, skin, nose and lungs.

Wood

Wood that is affected by mold growth or staining can usually be cleaned effectively using the wet scrubbing methods described at the beginning of this section. This kind of damage is common on wooden windowsills where moisture condenses due to poorly insulated windows. Correct the source of the problem and dry the wood thoroughly (check it using the plastic patch test outlined earlier in Part II, see p. 15). Finish the windowsill appropriately. Structural wood, such as joists or framing, does not need further finishing. To prevent mold from growing again, keep the wood dry.

If cleaning with detergent and water does not remove mold, try sanding the surface with a vacuum sander (simultaneous vacuuming and sanding). Do not attempt to sand without vacuuming. This method will not work if the mold has penetrated to the core of the wood. Severely moldy wood should be replaced.

Discoloration of wood may be due to wood-staining fungi (mold and sapstain fungi) or wood-decaying fungi (brown rot, white rot, soft rot). Mold growth on the surface can be removed by brushing, washing, sanding or planing the surface. Sapstain penetrates deeper into the sapwood and cannot be removed by surface treatments. Sapstain usually occurs during lumber manufacture. It does not weaken solid wood. On the other hand, wood-decaying fungi destroy the strength and other properties of the wood depending on the kind of fungus present and the length of the decay period. Specialists are required to identify the kind of wood-decaying fungi. Any visible sign may require removal.

Fungal growth on fine wood, such as millwork, furnishings and antiques, may require a professional to determine whether they can be repaired and the finishes saved.

Concrete and masonry

Walls

While dampness from water seepage may be a relatively common problem on unpainted concrete and masonry walls, mold rarely affects these materials. This is because of the high salt concentration that develops on the surfaces of these materials in the form of **efflorescence** (see p. 66).

Problems may develop, however, where excessive relative humidity condenses on cool basement walls of porous concrete and masonry that have been painted. If water penetration has been ruled out as a cause of the dampness problem, the best solution is to remove the affected paint and other surface debris and then to use a dehumidifier continuously in the space.

Where moisture enters the foundation from the outside, solve the problem by having a dampproofing membrane affixed and sealed to the wall on the exterior side (difficult but most effective) and proper drains installed around the foundation. When the outside has been excavated, rigid insulation such as extruded polystyrene can be installed. The combination of dampproofing, drainage and exterior insulation keeps the walls warm and prevents moisture entry. Installing dampproofing is complicated and best left to professionals with experience in these procedures.

The typical method used for finishing basements on the interior side (consisting of polyethylene-to-grade against the foundation, insulation, polyethylene vapour retarder and drywall) creates cavities where mold can start to grow.

Concrete floors

Concrete basement floors in older houses may allow dampness to enter the house, either through tiny cracks or directly through the concrete floor slab. As described earlier, dampness migrating through a concrete floor slab usually appears as transient patches of darkening whose location may vary based on the prevailing weather or from season to season. Short of installing a new, properly dampproofed floor (similar to the above description of wall dampproofing), the only way to reduce basement dampness is through dehumidification combined with efforts to prevent rainwater entry around the foundation.

Under no circumstances should carpeting ever be installed directly on a concrete basement floor. Applying painted sealants to basement concrete floors is usually ineffective, because of problems of inadequate adherence.

Keep surfaces warm and ensure good air distribution. Where cardboard boxes have been placed in direct contact with the floor, there is likely to be residual mold damage on the concrete. Remove this mold by scrubbing and mopping with the cleaning solutions described above. Once clean, run a dehumidifier constantly until the floor has dried. Then run the dehumidifier during the spring to fall to maintain sufficiently low relative humidity to prevent mold problems.

Earth basement floors

The most effective way to deal with mold problems associated with an earth floor in the basement or crawl space is to encapsulate the soil by installing a proper concrete floor slab. Plastic may provide a reasonable barrier to mold spores and moisture but does little to contain volatile organic compounds generated by molds growing beneath the plastic. By holding moisture in the soil, plastic sheeting can actually stimulate mold growth and exacerbate mold odour problems. Accordingly, installing a proper concrete floor slab is the recommended method for dealing with mold problems in earth-floor basements.

If you have to encapsulate a gravel, sand, earth or rock floor with plastic sheeting, use only heavy plastic such as 6-mil polyethylene. Cover the floor completely with a continuous sheet of plastic and seal it to the walls. Once the plastic has been laid and sealed, hold it in place with regularly placed bricks or blocks. Provide paving stones to walk on to prevent ripping the plastic. At the same time, improve the drainage around the house.

Cold rooms, root cellars and wine cellars

Conditions for storing root vegetables (for example, low temperature, high relative humidity) are conducive to mold growth. To make matters worse, many people store vegetables in cardboard boxes, which can become heavily contaminated by mold. In general, it is not a good idea to keep an indoor root cellar unless you are able to isolate it from the rest of the house by having an outdoor entrance.

A better idea is to install a second refrigerator in the basement and convert the cold room or root cellar to a conditioned space. Remove all drywall and insulation. Clean or remove moldy wood, seal wall openings (vents), and clean all surfaces with detergent and water. Remove the door or keep it open to the rest of the basement. Provide heat and dehumidification to the area.

Wine cellars may not pose problems to the extent that root cellars and cold rooms do, because they require only a slightly lower than ambient temperature (for example, 10–12°C, though up to 18°C may be acceptable for storing wine as long as the temperature does not fluctuate abruptly). It is important to maintain good airflow and ensure that the area is adequately dehumidified in the summertime. Most modern wine bottles seal the cork with a drop of wax or a foil capsule. Wines so bottled are more resistant to drying and can be stored safely at low relative humidity.

Tiles

The tiles and grout in shower stalls and tub surrounds in bathrooms are very favourable places for molds to grow.

Fortunately, these molds, although they cause discoloration, are not hazardous to health. They are best removed by scrubbing with detergent and water.

To prevent mold growth on bathroom tiles and grout, squeegee or wipe the tiles following a bath or shower. Run the bathroom exhaust fan for a while to help dry the surfaces.

Mold growth on tiles and grout

Carpets

Carpets can affect indoor air quality for three main reasons:

1)   They have a huge effective surface area (equal to the total surface area of all of the individual carpet fibres, which may be thousands of times greater than the actual floor area).

2)   They accumulate dirt and mold spores.

3)   They naturally trap and retain moisture
     (for example, when installed on a cold floor).

Unlike obvious mold growth on walls or window sills, mold in a carpet is hidden. Stains resulting from water damage should be taken as evidence that a mold problem exists until proven otherwise.

Carpets can store much more mold debris than any other kind of surface or covering. This material can be released into the air when a carpet is walked on or cleaned. Carpets should never be installed on any floor that is likely to become damp or wet (for example, kitchens, bathrooms, basements).

Moldy carpets

Scrap any carpet that gets wet and has remained moist for longer than 48 hours. It is virtually certain to contain mold due to incomplete or excessively prolonged drying. Expensive or rare carpets may be dry-cleaned by a specialist, but the cost will be considerable and some shrinkage or distortion may result. Expensive area rugs may merit the cost of cleaning, but ordinary carpets generally do not.

Similarly, scrap any moist carpet that emits a musty odour when carefully smell-tested at one to two inches above the surface as it can justifiably be considered moldy. Very old carpets or those that have been in a house with a severe mold problem are best dealt with as though they were moldy.

When you discard carpeting suspected of containing mold growth, be aware of the need to protect yourself and other occupants of the home from breathing mold spores. Move any people who may be abnormally sensitive to molds, such as young children or the elderly, out of the house. Wear a mask, gloves and eye protection. Work slowly and avoid sudden or violent movements. Wherever possible, it is best to cut the carpet into smaller pieces, place these pieces in bags, and remove the bagged material. Once the carpet is removed, damp- mop the floor with clean warm water containing a bit of unscented detergent. You can follow with a vinegar solution (1 cup per gallon or 250 ml per 4.5 litre). Repeat the mopping with clean water and then allow the floor to dry completely using a dehumidifier or vigorous ventilation with dry outdoor air if conditions allow.

Carpets of uncertain condition

Carpets that have not been damp in the past and that exhibit a slight musty odour on close-range, smell-testing may have absorbed mold odours from being close to moldy materials. Several options may be tried in this case. To start with, a careful vacuuming of the entire surface area, as described above, may alleviate the problem. Sprinkle baking soda liberally on the carpet. Leave overnight or longer, and then vacuum thoroughly.

If this does not succeed, another method involves steam-cleaning followed by very rapid drying (sometimes called dry steam-cleaning). Remember that any water-based cleaning method risks shrinking or distorting the carpet. Steam-cleaning should be done by a professional and the room should be well ventilated with very dry outdoor air. Ideally, the carpet should be dried completely within several hours. Under no circumstances let it remain damp longer than 12 hours.

A third technique is to have carpets removed and cleaned professionally using either dry or wet methods. Off-premises cleaning is often effective but only worthwhile for very valuable carpets or those covered under warranty. In the end, if the carpet retains a musty odour there may be no alternative but to discard it.

Anti-fungal carpet treatments are not recommended.

Carpets in good condition

If carpets are in a house that is or may be moldy, but they are not obviously contaminated or musty, it is still wise to have them thoroughly cleaned, preferably by careful vacuuming as described above. Use wet-cleaning methods carefully, and make sure that the carpet dries out completely within several hours of cleaning to avoid problems.

Contents

Mattresses and bedding

Because we spend many hours in close proximity to mattresses and bedding, we must apply higher standards to these materials than to other household items and furnishings. Even in the absence of dampness, mattresses are notorious havens for mold spores and dust mites. The combination of nightly warmth and humidity together with an ample supply of shed skin flakes creates an ideal habitat for the mites and fungi. Under normal circumstances, changing bedding at one- to two-week intervals avoids the buildup of populations of these unwanted inhabitants. Replace pillows annually. Note, however, that potentially hazardous levels of molds and dust mites can develop in mattresses that are exposed to abnormal dampness, such as may arise after a flood or under conditions of high humidity.

Plush toys should be considered as bedding because they are often used as pillows or otherwise held close to children's faces.

Moldy mattresses and bedding

If mattresses have obvious mold growth, smell musty or are badly water-stained, discard them. It is not possible to clean a mold-contaminated mattress because the contents cannot be accessed directly. It is not cost-effective to attempt to rehabilitate a mattress. Discard mattresses, pillows or bedding that have been stored in wet basements or crawl spaces. The health-risk of using these items far outweighs the cost of replacing them.

Mattresses in uncertain condition

It is reasonable to attempt to clean mattresses that have suffered minor damage from clean water—not dirty water—as long as they are not moldy or musty smelling. Immediately following the water damage, dry the mattress thoroughly in the sun for several hours, rotating it periodically. Once dry, sprinkle the mattress liberally with baking soda to absorb odours and allow it to sit for several hours. Then carefully go over it with a vacuum cleaner. Treating a water-damaged mattress can take a few days if the sun is intermittent. Remember to bring the mattress indoors during damp weather and at night. Mattresses may become moldy if drying is prolonged due to weather conditions that are unsuitable for drying.

Mattresses in good condition

If a fresh dry mattress is in a house suspected of having mold problems, go over it with a vacuum cleaner and air it out. It is helpful to place the mattress in full sunlight for several hours, turning it occasionally so that both sides are well exposed.

Clothing

Clothing must be clean and uncontaminated, since it comes into contact with our skin. Like other textile items, clothing has a tendency to absorb moisture and odours. Storing clothing in the presence of dampness invites mold contamination. Prior to any attempt to remove mold soiling from clothing, read the label directions carefully. You should not attempt to remove stains from clothes that stipulate "dry-clean only." You run the risk of ruining these items if you attempt to clean them yourself. It is important for all dry-cleaned clothes to be aired out well prior to bringing them back indoors. Many of the chemicals used in dry-cleaning may be hazardous to human health if traces of these chemicals remain in the clothing.

Moldy clothing

Clothing with mold odours or minor mold spotting can usually be cleaned effectively with a good detergent, as long as the damage has not weakened the textile fibres. Laundry detergents that contain enzymes and brightening agents are most effective at removing mold staining. Bleach may be used on stubborn mold stains, followed by washing and rinsing. If the clothing does not pass the sniff test or if it remains stained, repeat the wash-and-rinse cycle. Dry the washed clothing rapidly and thoroughly, and store it in a clean, dry area. Items that cannot be washed should be dry-cleaned and aired, then stored. A thorough decontamination may require more than one cleaning. If staining or odour remains after two attempts, discard the item. Leather items should always be examined professionally if you think there is a chance they can be saved. Air all items well in the sunshine after cleaning. There may be no alternative to discarding clothing in which the textile fibres have been weakened. Well-worn and fragile clothing items are more susceptible to fibre breakdown.

Clothing in uncertain condition

Clothing that smells mildly musty and does not look water-stained should be washed well or dry-cleaned, as above, and then tested for residual mold odour. Airing in the sunshine is a good finishing touch.

Clothing in good condition

Clothing from a mold-troubled house that does not smell musty should be aired in the sun before being stored in a clean dry area. If in doubt, it never does any harm to clean clothing as a precautionary measure.

Drapery

Drapes, particularly the insulating variety, can become heavily contaminated with mold if they are used to conserve energy where window insulation is poor. Cold or leaky windows may build up condensation during the winter, which may be transferred to the drapes and walls. Drapes, like carpets, have a large effective surface area and can retain a great deal of moisture that may support mold growth. Mold spores and by-products can then be released from dirty drapes when they are warmed by sunlight. Drapes that have obvious mold growth and those that smell musty should be treated alike.

Moldy drapes

The best treatment for minor mold is to wash the drapes with a good detergent with some bleach added. Alternatively, have them dry-cleaned by a professional who is aware of methods for removing mold. Double washing or dry-cleaning will likely be required in most cases for the successful removal of staining. Air the drapes for several hours in the sun before bringing them back indoors. If a musty odour persists even after cleaning, you may have to replace the drapes; as well, the sources of excessive condensation or of mold must be corrected.

Drapes in uncertain condition

If drapes have been exposed to indoor air that is contaminated with mold, clean and air them to remove any residual contamination that may cling to the fibres. Cleaning can be done effectively either with a detergent that promotes complete wetting, or by dry-cleaning. Air the drapes well before bringing them back indoors.

Drapes in good condition

If there is no trace of mold smell or signs of water staining, a simple airing in the sun should suffice.

Upholstered Furniture

Upholstered furniture, like bedding, can retain dust and mold, spewing contaminants into the air when the articles are used or cleaned. Accordingly, if you wish to retain items that have been subject to moisture damage, it is important that they be considered carefully and treated appropriately.

Moldy upholstery

Like bedding, furniture that shows any degree of mold growth, or items that have remained damp for longer than 48 hours, should be discarded. Similarly, items that do not show obvious mold damage or dampness but cannot be rid of musty odours by vacuum cleaning and sun-drying should be discarded. Valuable items can be decontaminated by stripping off and discarding the contaminated covering and filling, followed by re-upholstery.

Upholstery in uncertain condition

If the item is clean and dry but has been exposed to airborne mold spores, it may still take on a moldy odour. A liberal sprinkling with baking soda a few hours prior to vacuum cleaning may help to remove persistent mold odours in all but the worst cases. Removing the cloth covering from the bottom and back of a chair or sofa may help in the cleaning process and significantly improve the chances of saving a piece of upholstered furniture. Then air-out the item thoroughly in the sun, and rotate it periodically to expose all surfaces to the sunlight. Follow this treatment with a final vacuum-cleaning. If the above is not successful, then re-upholstery or disposal are the only safe options.

Upholstery in good condition

In any house with a known or suspected mold problem, thoroughly vacuum clean all surfaces, especially upholstered ones, even if no moldy odours are present. Then thoroughly air all surfaces in the sunshine, with all sides exposed to sunlight.

Books and Papers

Paper products are made of cellulose, a highly favourable growth medium for molds. Paper products are moreover strongly absorbent, can store large amounts of moisture and are resistant to drying. This combination of properties makes paper stored in damp conditions especially susceptible to mold damage. Cleaning can be attempted on paper materials that show minor mold growth or that smell musty, depending on the extent of mold growth and the value of the article.

Recently wet paper

Moldy paper is one of the most difficult materials to clean. You can prevent mold growth on paper materials that get wet if they are dried rapidly and thoroughly within 24 hours of wetting. Discard non-valuable materials. Freeze materials that you want to save that you are not able to dry right away. Frozen materials will not grow mold. Find a conservator who does cleaning and drying for libraries and museums to dry your materials. You can dry loose sheets of paper by carefully removing excess water with a blotter and air drying or drying them in full sunlight.

Moldy books

Discard any books or other paper articles that show visible mold in the form of black or brown fuzzy growth, greenish powdery spots or reddish-to-violet stains on some or all of the pages. If the materials contain critical information, photocopying may be an option, but take care to prevent inhalation and skin exposure. If you choose to photocopy contaminated materials, wear a proper face mask and gloves. Do your photocopying in an isolated area that can be cleaned up by a combination of HEPA vacuum cleaning and damp-wiping once the process has been completed. If the materials are valuable in their existing form (for example, rare books) a library conservator may be able to repair them. The costs for repairing mold-contaminated books, however, are often considerable.

Books in uncertain condition

The presence of fox-marks, also known as **foxing** (faint brownish mottling on the faces of the pages) may be the result of dampness reacting with chemicals in the paper or ink. While foxing itself is not hazardous, it is evidence that books have been stored improperly. One way to deal with fox-marked or musty or earthy-smelling books is to place them open in full sunlight, periodically turning the pages to air them out. If the pages are very dry, you can try dusting the pages with baking soda to help absorb the musty odour. Once the articles have been aired for a few days, you can remove the baking soda by brushing it out with a soft brush, such as an artist's brush or a cosmetic brush. Be sure to perform this process outdoors wearing gloves and a dust mask to avoid breathing in the baking soda dust.

If this technique does not eliminate the musty or earthy odour from the materials, a final option is to have them treated using ozone in a proper facility (not in your house) by an experienced professional. **Note that ozone is a very harmful gas and is not approved for remedial treatment of mold in houses**. In addition to its potential health effects, ozone inside your home can degrade materials in your house (plastics, carpets and furnishings made of synthetic materials). The breakdown can continue even if the ozone has been stopped.

Books in good condition

Books and papers that have remained dry but may have come into contact with airborne spores require no special cleaning or treatment. The presence of low levels of mold spores on these materials does not put them at risk of becoming moldy. However, any paper materials are at risk of becoming moldy if they get wet and are not promptly dried—even if they are perfectly clean to begin with. If you must store books or papers, do so in a place where the relative humidity is below 50 per cent. If you place books inside an airtight box (preferably plastic), include a container of **desiccant** in the storage box and change it regularly, such as every six months.

Valuable papers and books

If books or papers are very valuable, have them treated by companies that do drying and cleaning for libraries and museums. These companies may recommend against using baking soda, since it does not always come off during the wiping or vacuuming and may add to staining problems if the paper is very wet. The wiping process may also remove some ink.

It may be desirable to copy legal papers and have them certified as legal copies or surrogate originals, then to destroy the damaged originals, or at least to dry and store contaminated papers in a sealed container with a **desiccant**.

Other household items

Any surfaces that visibly collect dust may also collect mold spores and moldy debris, so you should clean them. Even vertical surfaces may also collect and hold dust, dirt and mold spores by static attraction, chemical adhesion or other means. In the tradition of a good spring cleaning (whether it's spring or not), clean these surfaces as well. Clean non-paper materials with a simple solution of warm soapy water (for example, 1 teaspoon liquid dishwashing detergent per gallon of warm water). Do not use too much soap or detergent because it will leave a surface film that will promote future soiling. Wipe with a cloth dampened in clean water and let dry.

Some materials, such as leather shoes, bags and boots, cannot be effectively decontaminated once they become moldy, and must be discarded. Certain types of sports equipment, including solid items such as skis, racquets, etc., can be washed, then carefully and quickly dried (but not so quickly as to cause them to crack) and then aired in the sun. Treat sporting items made of fabric as clothing.

Summary

Bear in mind that to completely eliminate every single spore is impossible. Minor levels of residual spores on otherwise uncontaminated surfaces neither predispose these items to mold growth in the future nor pose a risk to the health of people using the items. By all means clean these items to reduce the levels of fungal spores adhering to them, but there is no point in being obsessive about it. Your clean-up efforts should be based on the following core principles:

*   prioritize your approach to cleaning up
*   carry out your clean-up systematically, completing one area before moving to the next
*   discard mold-affected items that cannot be cleaned
*   clean items that have come into contact with airborne spores

Remember that sources of superfluous moisture must be corrected without delay; otherwise, mold will grow back and your efforts to clean up will have been wasted.

APPENDIXES

APPENDIX A: MOLD BIOLOGY

Molds are microscopic members of the category of living things called **fungi**. Molds may be familiar to you as the fuzzy spots on long-forgotten leftovers, the powdery blemishes on ailing houseplants or the dusty speckles on books consigned to a damp cellar. They are some of nature's greatest specialists at causing moist **organic matter** (material derived mostly from life-forms, such as plants, animals and in some cases other fungi) to decompose. Molds invade these materials by means of tiny filaments or threads that are 50 times thinner than a human hair. These threads, known as **hyphae** can bore through virtually any damp organic material using a combination of mechanical force and corrosive chemicals called **enzymes**. Mold enzymes digest the host material, releasing nutrients that the mold absorbs to fuel its growth. A fuzzy mass of hyphae large enough to be visible without a microscope is called a **mycelium**.

The seeds of molds, known as **spores**, are about 500 times smaller than the head of a pin, much too small to be seen without a microscope. Many molds take advantage of the natural movement of the air to carry their spores from place to place. As a result, mold spores are most abundant in the outdoor air during the summer months. In fact, in an average breath of fresh, outdoor air (equivalent in volume to two drinking glasses) you might expect to inhale up to 100 tiny mold spores. Under normal circumstances the levels of mold spores in the air in your house should be roughly one tenth of those in the outdoor air.

WHAT ARE FUNGI?

Fungi are one of five "kingdoms" into which biologists divide all living things. The other kingdoms are Plants, Animals, Bacteria and Protists (microscopic, amoeba-like organisms). Biologists are still uncertain about classifying viruses as living things, so for now they are dealt with outside this framework. Thus fungi are neither plants nor animals nor bacteria nor viruses and are unrelated to these groups.

Several features set **molds** and other fungi apart from other life forms.

- In a few ways they are like animals:

  - Their cell walls are made of chitin, the same material that makes up the exoskeletons of insects (in contrast, plant cell walls are made of cellulose, the same material that we use to make paper).

  - They lack chlorophyll, the green pigment that plants use to harvest energy from the sun and instead must derive their nutrition from other living (or at least formerly living) things.

- In other ways, they resemble plants:

  – In both fungal and plant cells, the cellular contents are enclosed in a flexible cell membrane, which is encased inside a rigid cell wall, like a plastic bag filled with water placed inside a cardboard box. Animal cells, on the other hand, universally lack cell walls and have only cell membranes.

  – Fungi lack mobility. Like plants, fungi are pretty much bound to their place of growth until their demise, in contrast to animals, which walk, crawl, slither or fly from place to place.

Some other groups of fungi that you might recognize are:

- **Mushrooms**, some of which dot the autumn forest floor, are the brokers of scarce soil nutrients that support the trees towering above; others grow in open meadows in ever-widening, ancient arcs whose full circumference can only be seen from an airplane.

- **Puffballs**, marshmallow-like sacs that range in size from golf ball to soccer ball, live on fragments of dead wood or in open pastures. At maturity, each puffball becomes so packed full of spores that if every spore were to reproduce successfully from only a single puffball, enough puffballs would result to cover the entire surface of the earth.

- **Yeasts**, microscopic fungi whose beneficial members are essential to food and beverage processing, and whose harmful members can cause life-threatening infections.

- **Lichen**, best known in their rubbery, preserved form as the trees and shrubs of toy train sets, lichens are a biological joint-venture between fungi and microscopic plants called algae. Lichens inhabit exposed tree bark and rocks where their patches grow so imperceptibly slowly that they might advance only one to two millimetres per year.

WHAT ARE MOLDS?

Molds make up a small category of fungi. People often use "mold" and "mildew" interchangeably in reference to the fuzzy spots described at the beginning of this section. Properly speaking, however, **mildews** are fungi that cause diseases of plants, producing powdery white blotches on leaves. You can observe spots of mildew on many different kinds of plants, such as turf grass, roses and lilac bushes, in late summer through autumn. You cannot observe spots of mildew, however, on bathroom tiles, soggy cardboard or windowsills, since these are the domains of mold.

To paraphrase the 17th-century English philosopher Thomas Hobbes, the lives of molds are nasty, brutish and short. Of all fungi, molds are adapted to grow and reproduce with the most astonishing speed, often waging chemical warfare against other molds during fierce territorial disputes. Some molds can complete their entire brief life span in less than a single day. Although even the speediest of molds grows at only one-billionth the speed of a car travelling along a downtown street, they still grow fast enough to be observed in real time using a microscope of reasonable quality. The speediness and competitive nature of molds have earned them notoriety as the "weeds" of the fungal world.

MYCOLOGY: THE STUDY OF FUNGI

Just as fungi are unique in comparison to other life forms, so the study of fungi is a discipline unto itself. The scientific study of molds and other fungi such as lichens and mushrooms is known as **mycology**; and the scientists who specialize in this field are called mycologists. This field is not the same as microbiology, which is the name commonly used for the study of bacteria. The field of **microbiology** developed alongside medicine, and most human pathogenic micro-organisms are bacteria. Microbiologists, also called **bacteriologists**, usually devote only a minor part of their formal education to studying certain fungi, and then only those fungal species relevant to human and animal infection. Mycology, on the other hand, is a much older field of study than microbiology and is a sub-discipline of **Botany** (Plant Biology). Thus mycologists are botanists specialized in the study of fungi and, to an extent, plant diseases, most of which are caused by fungi, not bacteria.

APPENDIX B:
SURVEYING INDOOR MOISTURE AND MOLD

The following extra information can help guide you as you complete **Checklist B**. If you are unsure of any of the terms used in this text, check for them in the Glossary at the beginning of this guide.

The goals of your investigation are:

1) To identify areas that are damp or that may have been affected by leakage or condensation.

2) To tally up the amount of area that is affected by mold growth.

Be sure to set aside a few hours to carry out this detailed survey. Follow the procedure described below, starting first with the exterior of the house and progressing to the interior. It is important at this stage to ensure that you take care not to disturb any areas or materials that might be affected by mold. Leave everything intact for the time being in order to gain a clear idea of the extent of the damage and why it occurred. Be thorough during your investigation. Because of your familiarity with your house, you may unknowingly overlook important problem signs. To avoid this, it may help to have a friend who is not as familiar with your house and its contents to assist you. Remember to consider both current and past moisture damage and mold even if it may no longer seem to be a problem. It is also important to take note of the environmental conditions (for example, indoor and outdoor temperatures, humidity, and weather), which affect leakage and condensation.

The tools required for your investigation are described in **Part I** of this guide. In addition, people who are very sensitive or ill and who are unable to enlist a friend or family member to carry out the investigation for them, should take the exposure precautions described earlier in **Part III** of this guide (see Protecting Yourself p. 33).

EXTERIOR INSPECTION

The integrity of the structure of a house is essential to keeping water out, and is your house's first line of defense against moisture and mold problems. Some of the points discussed in this investigation may not be readily observable at all times. Water problems caused by rainwater leakage, such as from faulty eavestroughs or foundation leaks, may best be observed when it rains, or shortly afterwards.

Knowing your house means watching how it performs in good weather as well as bad. Next time it is raining or snowing, put on your outdoor clothing and step outside to see what your house is doing. Is water leaking from places it shouldn't? Does rainwater drain away from your house's foundation? Does snow melt away from certain areas of the roof and not from others? Does ice build up in your eavestroughs? Sometimes the most obvious problems go unnoticed.

When examining the house's exterior, it is best to start at the top and work your way down.

Roof

Most sloped roofs are covered by asphalt shingles. Other types of water-shedding materials are also used, including slate, clay tile, cedar and metal. Asphalt shingles on a pitched roof should lie flat. Surface deterioration, lifting, curling or missing shingles are problem signs and indicate the need for repair or replacement.

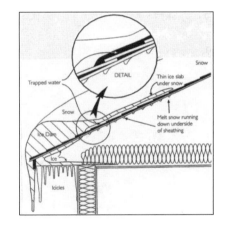

In houses with sloped roofs and poor attic insulation and/or excessive leakage of house air into the attic, **ice dams** can form on the roof in the wintertime. This happens when heat from the house warms the roof sufficiently to melt snow-cover, allowing the water to begin to run off. At the eaves, the roof extends beyond the walls of the house and the roof surface remains cold because there is no heating from below. The water then cools and re-freezes to form an **ice dam** at or near the eave. A layer of ice eventually forms on the roof sheathing above the ice dam. Melting snow is trapped between the ice slab and roof shingles. If your house suffers from ice dams, arrange to have the roof repaired and the underlying problem corrected. Also, walls below such leaks are vulnerable to mold growth and should be inspected and repaired. For more information on ice dams, consult the CMHC publication *About Your House: Attic Venting, Attic Moisture and Ice Dams, 62034.*

Flat roofs are protected by a system of waterproof membranes. Most flat roofs are constructed with some form of roof membrane built up from multiple layers of roofing felt (or asphalt-based membrane plies) laminated together with asphalt or asphalt-based adhesives. The top surface may be covered with gravel, mineral granules or aluminized paint. Newer roof membranes consist of single-ply plastic or rubber-based materials. Flat roofs may also use metal coverings.

Look for areas of surface deterioration, cracking, blistering, open seams or uneven surface conditions. Water pooling on a flat roof is also problematic, particularly in the event of a leak, whereby the pooled water drains into the house.

Eaves and eavestroughs

Eaves, the parts of the roof that extend beyond the walls of the house, help protect against water entry where the roof and wall meet. In most houses, rainwater that drains from the roof is collected in **eavestroughs** or rain gutters and drained away by downspouts to storm drains, or onto the surface at least 2 m (6 ft.) from the house. This system should function without leakage or overflow. Water overflowing from the eavestroughs may indicate a blockage. Regular removal of leaves and other debris from eavestroughs is essential to ensure that the downspouts do not become clogged. Any separation of the eavestroughs from the roof can also cause leakage and damage to the structure of the house.

It is common to see houses with **downspouts** terminating above the ground. Extending the downspout away from the house is a simple step to move water away from the foundation. Many older urban houses have downspouts that enter straight into the ground and empty directly into the sewer system. If the drainpipes become blocked or damaged, water can back up into the basement. Disconnecting your downspouts from the sewer system and attaching an extension to drain water well away from the foundation can prevent this problem and at the same time reduce the amount of stormwater handled by the sewer system.

Chimney

Chimneys can allow water to leak into houses. Masonry chimneys should have a concrete cap to direct water away from the flue and to protect the brick joints from water. The point at which the chimney joins the roof should be protected with a **flashing** and a chimney saddle (see **Flashing**). If you are in doubt about the condition of your chimney, have it checked by a professional.

Flashing

Flashings prevent moisture entry where different kinds of building materials meet, at junctions or "transitions" between horizontal and vertical materials. The flashing should include a waterproof membrane flashing sealing the underlying materials against moisture penetration, covered with a thin metal flashing to channel water away. Flashings must be used at the junction of roofs and walls or of roofs and chimneys, in roof valleys, over window and door openings, and in other critical areas.

Cladding/siding

The material that covers the outside walls of your house is usually referred to as **cladding**. There are many forms—wood, vinyl and metal siding, masonry and stucco. Masonry, metal and vinyl siding are used extensively in home construction because they require little maintenance and come with factory-finished surfaces. The cladding material used on your house must be able to protect it adequately, particularly in wet areas of the country where wind-driven rain is common. Cracking, surface deterioration, or loose cracked caulking may indicate a point where water can penetrate.

Stucco exteriors vary considerably based on their age. Cement-based stucco is usually between 10 and 25 mm thick (approx. 0.4 to 1 in.) and was most commonly applied to a low-cost masonry surface or to a wood-frame structure. These systems can be very moisture-resistant when in good condition. Minor breaches in stucco finishes of this sort, however, can lead to significant water problems indoors, so if you notice cracking or chipping, repairs are in order. Take special note of the sealant condition at window joints, control joints (deliberately placed spaces or gaps in the exterior to allow for thermal expansion) and at details and corners.

More recently, stucco materials containing plastics (polymer), which are considerably thinner than traditional stucco (for example, 2 to 6 mm or 0.07 in. to 0.23 in.) are being used. These materials are applied over reinforcing wire mesh, and commonly incorporate some form of rigid insulation applied to the exterior surface of the home. This type of stucco is more correctly referred to as exterior insulation and finish system (EIFS). The polymer additives used with this system are intended to add flexibility to the finish and thus reduce cracking and the resulting admission of moisture, but they are just as vulnerable (and in some cases more vulnerable) than other types of stucco to moisture ingress at failed caulking joints or at transitions to roofs and windows.

Windows

Windows are one of the areas where water is most likely to penetrate into buildings. Check to make sure that the caulking seal around windows is intact and has no gaps or cracks. Note any signs of water staining that might suggest that seepage is occurring.

For more information on window problems and solutions, consult the CMHC fact sheet, *About Your House: Windows,* 62031.

Foundation walls

Concrete and masonry

In newer houses, concrete and masonry foundation walls are normally made dampproof using a heavy coating of a tar-like substance or a plastic film that extends from the soil line to the base of the foundation wall below the ground. These coatings protect the foundation wall against seepage that can occur after a rainstorm or from ordinary soil dampness. Basement foundations that extend below the local water table require waterproofing. The current (1995) National Building Code also requires that a free-draining layer extend from grade level to the footing drain or weeping tile directly adjacent to foundation walls. It is intended to provide a "preferential route" for water to follow down to the footing drains (as opposed to your basement).

Decorative plantings, trees and shrubs growing directly against a foundation wall may compromise dampproofing and cause leakage. Gardening activities that break up the earth at the base of the foundation wall can cause water to become channeled rather than to drain away, leading to basement moisture. Move garden beds away from the foundation to prevent these problems.

Preserved wood foundations

Preserved wood foundations (PWFs) are foundation systems built from pressure-treated lumber, typically preserved with chromated copper arsenate (CCA). PWFs may perform poorly in damp conditions. Furthermore, even under optimal conditions, the stability of CCA and the life expectancy of PWFs are unclear. Mold has been found to grow in CCA-preserved wood exposed to dampness (for example, foundations). Recent concern over the toxicity of CCA has compelled manufacturers to phase out the production of CCA-treated wood.

Drainage

Leakage along your foundation walls may be the result of cracked walls or damaged or missing dampproofing, waterproofing or drainage layers. If you live in an area with a high water table, you may have no other option but to excavate and repair. However, in many circumstances, the wall deficiency only becomes a problem when the surface drainage directs water toward the foundation walls.

The ground surrounding the house should slope so that rainwater drains away from the foundation. Walkways, patios or driveways that slope toward the house may cause water to pool against the foundation and result in basement leaks. In addition, when fitted with enough pipe, downspouts can direct rainwater well away from the house's foundation.

INTERIOR INSPECTION

In contrast to the exterior inspection, checking the interior of your house is a task best accomplished by starting at the bottom and working up. Let your observations from your exterior inspection help guide your efforts on the interior. As you proceed, you may find several different kinds of moisture problems affecting different areas. Don't stop looking if you find a problem. Be thorough. Remember that the first part of the investigation involves looking for moisture <u>and</u> mold. It is important to continue to be aware of both elements.

Basement

In past times the musty domain of spiders and coal bins, the basement in its modern version is considered an extension of the living space of a home. The success of basements in this regard, however, entirely depends on preventing moisture problems. While advances in construction materials and practices have helped immeasurably in achieving this goal, basements face three perils absent in the upper part of a house: 1) they are at the lowest point in the event of a flood; 2) their porous walls are in constant contact with moist soil; and 3) during the summer the temperature of the surrounding soil causes basement air to be cooler than air in the rest of the house or outside it. These three conditions make basements more susceptible to leakage and condensation than any other part of the house.

Wood framing

Most Canadian houses use wood-frame construction with the outside finished with siding or masonry and the inside walls finished with plaster or drywall. Areas of structural lumber may be evident in the basement of your house if it is unfinished. Wood is susceptible to fungal growth if it gets wet and remains damp.

The kinds of fungal problems that affect wood may be grouped into two general categories: **mold** and **rot**. **Mold** on wood usually presents itself as a superficial, usually dark-coloured fuzzy growth, typically on wood that is moist but not saturated. Most molds that cause this kind of discoloration on wood are allergenic but not nearly as hazardous as some of the mycotoxin-producing molds that grow on paper products.

Rot is caused by a different group of fungi more closely related to mushrooms. While rot fungi usually do not present much of a threat to human health, they can be disastrous to wood, in some cases reducing it to dust. There are two forms of rot, named for the colour that they cause in affected wood: **white rot** and **brown rot**. Sometimes, a leathery white or brownish sweating mass of fungus may also be present on affected wood. You can test the integrity of wood by probing it with your screwdriver. Severely rotted wood will yield readily to a gentle poke. One kind of brown rot, sometimes called "**dry rot**," is common in Europe, where it is has been recognized since antiquity as a scourge of buildings.

If there is no obvious fungal damage on the surface of wood, but you suspect dampness, check the wood using the plastic patch test (see p. 15) or with a moisture meter.

Unfinished interior sides of exterior walls

Chances are that the foundation walls of your house are made from one of two materials. Walls of houses more than 60 years old may be constructed from brick or stone held together by mortar. Newer houses typically have foundation walls made of formed concrete or concrete block. In either case, examine the wall for cracks. Hairline cracks up to 1/8 of an inch wide (3.175 mm) are usually not a problem as long as there is no sign of water leakage. Cracks that are wider than 1/4 of an inch (6.35 mm) may be a cause for concern. If a crack extends horizontally, it may indicate pressure from the surrounding soil, possibly the result of a high water table. Regardless of the crack size, if you notice moving or growing cracks, have a structural engineer examine them.

A common feature of moisture problems affecting foundation walls is the formation of fuzzy white spots that develop on the surface of poured concrete or masonry. This fuzzy growth, known as **efflorescence**, consists of delicate crystals of salts that form when salt-laden moisture migrates through concrete or masonry. Upon reaching the dry side of the wall, the moisture evaporates, leaving the salts behind to crystallize. If the process happens over a long period, a considerable amount of salt crystals may accumulate, which may be several centimetres in thickness. This same process is responsible for lime deposits that often accumulate around kitchen and bathroom faucets. You can test to see if the material is mineral salt by mixing it with a few drops of household vinegar to see if it bubbles or dissolves, signifying that it is mineral salt and not mold.

Paint on the surface of concrete or masonry walls may develop mold problems if the basement is humid. It is usually best to leave these surfaces unpainted, unless the proper exterior work has been done to prevent moisture from penetrating.

Finished interior sides of exterior walls

Inspecting a finished basement can be tricky because wall finishes may cover characteristic signs and symptoms of water leaks and other moisture problems. If you are in the fortunate position of having finished the basement yourself (or at least, having had it finished by someone else under your direction), then you may at least be familiar with the deficiencies of its pre-finished state. Even so, be aware that the driest basement may develop moisture problems resulting partly from the changed conditions following the enclosure of walls and floors. If you have moved into a house with a finished basement, you are starting from scratch in trying to determine what moisture problems it may have. Be aware that some unscrupulous real-estate agents or private owners may attempt to mask basement moisture problems with cosmetic improvements.

In basements, some wall-finishing materials tend to be much more susceptible to moisture and mold problems than others. Drywall is a poor choice for basement finishing projects. If the walls are painted or papered, it may be difficult to tell what wall-finishing material lies beneath. One useful method, however, is to inspect electrical outlets. Remove the cover. Do not stick your fingers or your screwdriver into the electrical box. If the walls are made from drywall, you should be able to see the paper facings and the core of gypsum in the cut-out hole for the electrical box. Determine if there is a vapour barrier (sheet of plastic) beneath the wallboard material. Check closely inside the electrical box for evidence of rust or corrosion, a typical symptom of moisture damage. Remember to replace the receptacle covers after you have completed this part of your investigation.

Note the location and extent of any obvious mold growth. Next, feel around the base of the interior side of all exterior walls. Crunchy or soft spots on drywall are signs of past or present water damage. Cool or clammy spots indicate current dampness. Examine the entire wall surface in good light. Be aware of any dimpling or subtle unevenness (like the surface of an orange peel) on painted drywall, or lines of discoloration or staining, especially on wood paneling, that would indicate past water damage. Also you might want to test several locations using either the tape test or the plastic patch test.

Floors and flooring

In most houses, the basement floor is made of concrete. Inspect the floor for cracks just as you did the interior sides of the exterior walls. Keep note of any signs of past or ongoing flooding which might include staining or tiny "dry riverbeds" converging at the lowest point in the floor (where the floor drain is located). Also, make note of any insects you see. Insects such as pill bugs, also known as sowbugs, which look like tiny armadillos, are common wherever there is moisture.

Floor coverings such as carpets and vinyl should not be placed directly on concrete floors. Soil moisture migrating through the concrete slab, or airborne moisture accumulating on the cool concrete surface, may provide sufficient conditions for mold to grow. These materials should be removed. An option for finishing a concrete floor is floor paint.

Basements or crawlspaces in older houses may have earth floors. Earth floors can be a source of significant moisture and mold problems in basements, as discussed in the clean-up section of this guide.

Floor drains

Just like the drain in your sink, each floor drain is attached to a pipe trap, which is supposed to prevent the backflow of sewer gases. Current building codes require that floor drains be primed (for example, automatically injected with water periodically) but, in some older homes, the water in the trap dries up, causing odour and moisture problems in the basement. There is no easy way to determine if a drain trap is dry. You can take a preventive approach to this problem by pouring water onto the drain frequently.

Sump

Sumps are predominantly used to collect water from the footing drains or weeping tiles. As the sump pit fills, an electrical pump operates intermittently to pump out the water. In houses where the basement extends below the local water table, sumps are installed to prevent the buildup of water pressure against the foundation. Sumps normally contain standing water, which can contribute moisture to the basement air. Cover the sump with a moisture-resistant cover such as plywood wrapped or lined with plastic.

Furnishings and stored items

Most people use the basement of their home for four main purposes: 1) living space 2) storage 3) laundry 4) hobby activities. The items that people put in their basements are usually associated with one of these categories.

Living space

Basements used as living space are typically furnished with a sofa and television, or sometimes with bedroom furniture. When basement furnishings become water-damaged, mold growth usually results. The risk of developing mold-related health problems is greater the more time occupants spend in contact with moldy furnishings. Water damage from saturation, which may follow a flood or leak, often leaves obvious water staining on upholstery and wood. Water damage from high humidity, however, is more difficult to assess. Upholstered materials that feel damp or clammy, or have a musty odour, are likely to have been exposed to high humidity and to have mold damage.

Storage

Some seasonal items, such as bicycles and patio furniture, are usually resistant to moisture damage. Other items such as clothing, tents, sports gear and other fabric-based objects are more susceptible.

Storing paper-based items like books, newspapers, magazines and photographs in the basement is a bad idea. This is also true for clothing and blankets. Paper and cardboard have a high capacity to absorb moisture from the air and to retain it even in conditions of fairly low relative humidity. These materials are hazardous when they get moldy. **Never store cardboard boxes directly on concrete basement floors.** If you must use your basement for storage, use resealable polyethylene bins instead of cardboard.

If stored materials have no obvious mold growth, check them out for water staining, then feel for dampness, and finally try the sniff test for mustiness. Use **Checklist B** to keep track of items that show even minor moisture damage.

Laundry

Many people use their basements at least in part for doing laundry. Laundry is a wet process and may contribute considerable moisture to the basement environment. Check for signs of unnecessary moisture. Make sure that water from the washing machine discharges properly into a laundry sink. Where possible, use pipe extensions to reduce splashing. Use cold water for washing whenever possible. Immersion in soapy cold water is also an effective way to kill dust mites (contrary to the popular notion, hot water is not necessary for this purpose). Cold-water washing reduces the amount of water vapour released and also conserves power. When the washing machine is not in use, leave the tub open so that any residual water can dry, which prevents molds and bacteria from growing inside the washing machine.

Check all the plumbing connections for leaks and drips. Be aware that a dripping laundry tub faucet will cause the bottom of the laundry tub to be wet, contributing to basement humidity problems. Look closely at the flexible lines that connect the washing machine to the water supply. Aside from storm water, the bursting of these lines is one of the most common causes of basement flooding. It is always best to use lines reinforced with braided steel.

Check the insulation on water pipes. **All water pipes supplying faucets, washing machines and water heaters should be wrapped with insulation.** Pipes delivering hot water are insulated to help conserve energy. Cold-water pipes, on the other hand, are insulated to prevent moisture from condensing on them and dripping.

The clothes dryer should be vented to the outdoors and this vent should be kept clear. Devices that allow you to vent your dryer back into the basement as a way to conserve heat and moisture are a bad idea under any circumstances. Avoid line-drying clothes indoors. To reduce static electricity, remove items from the dryer before they are fully dry. If sufficiently pre-dried in the dryer, the small amount of moisture given off in the final drying on a line inside may not be a large concern.

Tips on Reducing Indoor Relative Humidity

In the basement...

- Use a fan to circulate air in the basement
- Vent clothes dryer to the outdoors
- Do not hang clothes to dry in the basement
- Use a dehumidifier
- Eliminate absorbing materials, such as newspapers, clothes and aquariums
- Remove carpets
- Cover sump pit, if present
- Provide sufficient heat to the basement throughout the year (a small amount of heat outside of the heating season can help dry the basement)

Upstairs...

- Leave a gap of at least 5 cm (2 in.) between furniture and the interior sides of exterior walls
- Do not use humidifiers unless absolutely necessary
- Get rid of unnecessary water sources
- Promptly repair dripping faucets and all other water leaks
- Insulate cold exterior walls
- Avoid overcooling in the summer
- Install exhaust fans in the bathroom and kitchen and use them
- Wire exhaust fans to turn on whenever the room light is switched on
- Minimize clutter and furnishings that hold moisture
- Limit the number of plants and aquariums in the house

Hobbies

Many hobby activities take place in the basement and they use potentially harmful chemicals or generate byproducts such as moisture that can contribute to basement mold problems. As you walk through the basement of your house, consider how it is being used, if at all, for hobby activities. Be aware of the hazards that may be associated with these uses.

For instance, wood used for woodworking, like paper, is very absorbent. If it must be stored in the house, it should be elevated from the floor in an area where air can circulate freely around it. Individual boards should be adequately spaced to permit ventilation and prevent the trapping of air, which can lead to moisture damage and mold growth. The sawdust generated during woodworking is much more absorbent than whole wood. Do not allow this material to accumulate. Install a proper dust collection system situated near cutting tools. Other hobbies such as furniture refinishing, darkroom photography and horticulture can generate chemical vapours or moisture. Isolate areas used for these activities from the rest of the basement and provide adequately powered ventilation to the outdoors.

Basement mechanical systems

The mechanical systems found in your home are intended to provide heating, cooling, humidification and ventilation. Although you may not have specific equipment to provide each of the foregoing functions, current building codes require that you have a heating system and a ventilation system to ensure adequate fresh air. Most mechanical systems are located in the basement of your home, but they can also be found in an enclosed space within the garage, in the attic or in a main floor mechanical room or furnace room.

Heating systems

Three general types of heating systems are used in residential housing: 1) forced air systems 2) re-circulated hot water systems and 3) electric baseboard systems. The furnaces for the first two kinds are normally installed in the basement and are fuelled by natural gas, electricity or heating oil.

Forced air heating systems draw air in from the various floors by means of ducts (large conduits made of thin metal), heat the air, and then blow it back through a second set of ducts to supply heat to the house. The same unit may be equipped with a chilling coil connected to an outdoor compressor to provide cooling during the summer months. If this is the case, make sure that the ducts that carry chilled air do not have condensed moisture on their surfaces. Normally, the blower on a forced air unit operates only during heating or cooling, but in some cases it can act as a circulation or exhaust fan as well. Forced air units are equipped with filters that remove particles from the air. Change the furnace filters regularly and have a mechanical contractor maintain your system annually.

If your basement has moisture or mold problems, as an immediate but temporary measure, until you get the problem corrected, ensure that ducts and grilles in the basement are sealed to prevent air from being drawn from the basement and circulated through the rest of the house. The basement must be provided with an alternate source of heat (such as, electric baseboards).

Hot water radiator systems circulate water through a closed loop of pipes from the heating chamber (or boiler) to radiators on the upper floors and then back to the heater. Annual maintenance is required. Even though basement leakage of water from hot water heating systems is rarely a problem, you should make sure to check the connections. Be aware that a hot water heating system is distinct from your water heater (supplies faucets with heated water).

A common cause of mold growth in basements is reduced heating in these areas, resulting in cold spots, which in turn may lead to condensation. It is important that heat be provided to basements and that the air is adequately distributed to prevent local cold spots from forming.

Humidification and dehumidification

Forced air heating systems are often equipped with humidifiers, devices that are designed to contribute moisture to the air in the house. Humidifiers attached to furnaces are usually poorly maintained and more often than not reduce indoor air quality rather than improve it. It is best to have them disconnected. If you require increased humidity use a small, easily maintained, steam-type room humidifier operated intermittently as needed. People often mistakenly believe that more humidity is healthier. On the contrary, medical studies have indicated that home dampness and humidity may be an important factor in causing health problems such as asthma, especially in children. Symptoms of mucosal irritation by mold spores are often perceived to be due to excessive dryness. Using humidifiers will make the problem much worse. Most people generate enough moisture by regular daily activities and additional humidification is rarely necessary. Never use a humidifier without measuring the relative humidity beforehand to confirm that dryness really is a problem.

A far more useful appliance is the dehumidifier. It removes moisture from the air by drawing air over a chilled coil where it condenses and runs into a collection pan or directly down the drain (the latter is best). Air conditioning systems reduce humidity, but these units do not run continuously and are not primarily intended for dehumidification. While heat recovery ventilators (HRVs) reduce house humidity during the cold months, they can add moisture to the basement depending on the outside weather conditions at other times of the year. **Therefore, without exception, every house that has a basement should have a dehumidifier installed to reduce basement humidity during the spring, summer and fall.** The filter and coils of the unit require monthly cleaning to prevent the growth of molds on these surfaces.

Ventilation

Basements are notorious for clutter and poor air circulation. Humidity-related problems are likely to be worse in areas with trapped air or little air movement. To promote air movement, it is a good practice to keep basements as clean and clutter-free as possible. After you have done a thorough cleaning, you can also increase air circulation by letting the furnace fan run continuously or setting up a small fan and using a 24-hour timer to set it to run for a few hours periodically throughout the day and night.

Upper floors

As with basement moisture problems, water can affect the upper floors of a house in two main forms: 1) as liquid water from leakage and 2) as condensation. In both forms, moisture can lead to mold growth. In order to solve a moisture problem, it is important to figure out where the water is coming from.

Walls

Most wood-frame houses built since the 1950s are finished with drywall (gypsum board covered on both sides with paper). Older houses were finished with plaster applied on top of thin wooden slats called lath or drywall-like panels called gypsum lath. Houses that have had renovations have likely used drywall as the new wall-finishing material.

If you are uncertain about what a wall is made of, tap it lightly with your finger. Drywall produces a hollow sound, whereas plaster sounds dull. You can also look inside electrical outlets. Check closely inside the electrical box for evidence of rust or corrosion, a typical symptom of moisture damage. Remember to replace the receptacle covers after you have completed this part of your investigation.

Exterior walls

The outside (exterior) walls of a house function like our skin: 1) they keep the interior temperature of the house constant regardless of weather conditions prevailing on the outside; and 2) they provide a protective barrier against outdoor moisture moving into the house, while at the same time prevent indoor moisture from entering the wall assemblies. The exterior walls also support the floors and the roof. Because one side of these walls faces the outdoors, they are much more susceptible than interior walls to developing moisture and mold problems.

Look for any obvious water staining or mold growth on the wall surface. Keep in mind that moisture from condensation is usually worst in areas of the walls where the air is most still or cold, such as in corners near the ceiling or baseboard. Furnishings can also trap still pockets of air against the wall. This kind of problem happens when the indoor relative humidity is too high or the walls are poorly insulated and become too cold in the winter. If it is wintertime, feel the wall for cold spots that can indicate missing insulation.

Check the wall behind hanging pictures, large pieces of furniture or drapery. A flashlight, shining light at an angle, is the best tool for this job. The angled light clearly shows small patches of mold and light-coloured molds, which are sometimes not visible when viewed in direct light.

Actual leaking of water through the wall from the outside is another common problem. Areas beside and beneath windows are most susceptible. Gently push on the wall to feel for soft or crunchy spots that indicate moisture problems. If your rooms are carpeted, lift the carpet at the edge where it meets the wall and look underneath it. Sometimes staining on the walls, the subfloor or on the underside of the carpet indicates leakage.

Interior walls

Condensation is not normally a problem on the interior partition walls of a house, because these have roughly the same temperature on both sides. Condensation may develop near the ceiling on interior walls if there is poor attic insulation.

Many water problems that occur on interior walls result from roof leaks, accidents like overflowing sinks or toilets and water pipes that leak or condense inside the wall cavity.

Concealed damage

People often ask if mold is dangerous when it grows unseen inside the wall. Most experts agree that any mold growing inside a house, even inside a wall, can be bad for the occupants. Just how bad it may be is a function of how much damage there is and how easily the spores and other mold byproducts can enter the occupied space. Wind forces acting on exterior walls and pressure differences can cause air to move through the walls.

If you suspect that your house may have extensive mold growth inside the wall cavities, consider hiring a professional to check it out. A good visual inspection of the exposed surfaces of walls provides much information about the condition of the wall cavity.

Sometimes, however, mold growth on the inside of a wall leaves no obvious indicators. Detecting concealed mold growth remains one of the greatest challenges facing experts who conduct mold investigations. There are no reliable methods for making this determination short of opening up the walls and looking inside. The problem with this approach is that it is very intrusive and requires considerable repairs afterwards. Most experts prefer a scaled-down version. Inspectors use their observations of the undisturbed wall condition combined with their knowledge of where moisture damage is most likely to occur as a basis for cutting a few local exploratory holes into the most vulnerable wall areas. If they find mold in these areas, they continue inspecting larger and larger areas of wall to determine the extent of the damage. If mold is not found in the most vulnerable areas, an inspector could reasonably conclude that the wall is unlikely to contain widespread mold growth. Remember that no one can provide you with assurance that there is no mold except by taking your house apart, piece by piece. But try to put your situation into perspective. The amount of risk is related to the amount of mold, and a tiny spot means a tiny risk compared to a huge area of mold growth, indicating a much larger risk.

Ceilings

Water damage to the ceiling most often arises on the top floor of the house as the result of a roof leak or plumbing problem. Sometimes ceiling damage is not evident on the top floor but on one of the floors below. Condensation-related mold growth can also happen on the ceiling in places where the attic insulation is poor, causing the ceiling to be excessively cold during the winter. During your investigation, note any water-staining on the ceiling and any discoloration suggestive of mold growth.

Mold growth is also a common problem on bathroom ceilings. Poor ventilation is almost always the cause. An exhaust fan in the bathroom that ventilates to the outside of the house is the best way to disperse the moisture produced during bathing and showering. For the exhaust fan to operate effectively, there should be a gap of at least one inch (25.4 mm) between the floor and the bottom of the bathroom door.

Windows

Windows and the areas around them are especially susceptible to water damage. Water from the outside can penetrate easily through gaps or cracks in the caulking around windows. Leakage can also result when the window frames themselves allow moisture to penetrate between the frame joints or through the small space between the sashes and the frames. You should have noted any of these problems during your exterior inspection. Leaks of this sort can cause wetting that is generally worse on the wall and floor immediately below the window. Check these areas carefully.

Condensation on windows can be another source of moisture problems. During winter, when indoor relative humidity is high, condensed moisture "fog" forms on cold window surfaces (for example, single-glazed windows.) The moisture can drip and wet the windowsill and the area of wall below the window.

Ideally, windows should have minimal decorative coverings to promote good air circulation. Heavy drapes or other window dressings can make windows susceptible to condensation. Condensation on wooden windowsills often results in mold growth, appearing as powdery black, brown or reddish stains on the painted or unpainted sill surface. Most of the molds that grow in these circumstances are not especially hazardous and are easily cleaned up. To prevent window condensation in winter, reduce indoor relative humidity and upgrade windows with single glazing to more energy-efficient windows, such as argon gas-filled, double-glazed thermal units.

Ductwork

Inspect the ducts for dust build-up by removing floor registers and using a flashlight and mirror to take a look inside. You can also use a drain snake or flexible pipe with a damp rag secured to the end to swipe the duct. Vacuum the registers and the return air duct regularly. Arrange for professional duct cleaning if the dust accumulated on the inside is excessive, if you have just moved into the house or after a major renovation. Do not allow chemicals including so-called "antimicrobials" to be used in your ducts. These are of no use and may even be hazardous themselves.

Re-circulating water heating systems may be sensitive to leakage, especially systems involving radiators. Look for moisture damage on the floor around radiators. Water seepage around radiator valves indicates a need for maintenance and that seals, gaskets or valve packing need replacing.

Plumbing

As you continue to investigate the upper floors of your house, note the condition of the plumbing. Make sure that all the faucets are turned off and appliances are drawing no water, and then listen with your ear close to a water pipe or drain pipe. If you hear water running or if the gauge on the water meter is moving, a leak may be present. To locate the leak, try shutting off the water valve that supplies the water heater. If you no longer hear the sound of running water then the leak most likely involves a hot water heater. If the leaking sound continues, the cold water system is the likely culprit. (Remember to turn the water supply valve back on when you're finished.)

Open the cabinets under sinks and check the pipes and connections for leaks and dripping. Cold water pipes are susceptible to dripping from condensation during the summer. Check the condition of the supply lines (the flexible hoses made of plastic, copper, chrome, or braided steel that attach the faucet to the water supply pipes). Plastic supply lines are prone to pinhole leaks and sometimes burst. Installing braided steel supply lines on faucets and on the washing machine can help avoid costly flooding from burst lines.

Toilet tank

Look closely at the toilet tank. Does it show condensation in the summer? If your tank is not insulated along the inside, consider replacing it. You may also have a problem if the flapper valve inside the tank is leaky or if the water level in the tank is set too high, which causes the water inside the tank to keep filling and to remain cold. To check for this condition, add a few drops of food colouring to the water inside the toilet tank. Wait 30 minutes. If the colour of the water in the bowl changes, the flapper valve inside the tank may be leaking.

Caulking

Carefully inspect the condition of the caulking around the bathtub. Small gaps or cracks can cause leakage when the tub is used. Look around the sides of the tub and on the floor for any signs of leaking. Note any insects such as silverfish, centipedes, springtails and pill bugs, any of which indicate moisture problems.

Local exhaust ventilation

Exhaust ventilation to the outdoors should be installed for clothes dryers and range hoods as well as all bathrooms furnished with a tub or shower. Exhaust fans in bathrooms should be wired to the light switches so that they operate whenever the bathroom is used. The fan should run for at least 30 minutes following a bath or shower. Check the integrity of the exhaust vents in these locations. Exhaust vents may sometimes be points of entry for rainwater.

You can obtain more information on exhaust ventilation from the CMHC publication *About Your House: The Importance of Bathroom and Kitchen Fans,* 62037.

Appliances

Appliances such as washers, dishwashers, refrigerators and gas stoves can liberate a great deal of moisture during normal use.

Use a dehumidifier in any area of the house where the humidity is high. It is a good general rule to operate a portable dehumidifier in the basement as a preventive measure during spring, summer and fall, even if there are no apparent moisture problems. Air conditioners also provide effective dehumidification of the indoor air. Air conditioners that are of the incorrect size for an area (whether over- or under-powered) may cause problems. For instance, an overly powerful air conditioner may produce an unbalanced ratio of cooling relative to dehumidification, which causes the indoor air to be too humid and to feel clammy and cold. This imbalance may result in condensation and mold growth on surfaces in a direct line with the air conditioner vent, and possibly on the vent itself. Even though there is an air conditioner, we recommend using a dehumidifier in a house with a basement to reduce moisture when the air conditioner is not operating.

Limit the use of portable humidifiers. When you have to use a humidifier (for example, your physician has provided this advice for your child), follow this procedure: 1) measure the relative humidity to ensure that dryness is the problem and to establish the baseline humidity in your house 2) operate a steam-type humidifier, cycling it on and off until the right amount of humidity is present (must not exceed 45 per cent) 3) air the room out to dry between uses and 4) make sure that you clean the humidifier vigilantly at least every two to three days. **Do not, under any circumstances, operate a humidifier during the summer.**

Attic

The attic or roof space is the area of your house between the ceiling of the top floor and the roof. Not all houses have attics and, depending on the roof configuration, some houses may have more than one attic. But if your house has an attic, it is important to include it in your survey. Most often, there will be a covered cut-out in the ceiling on the upper floor of your house through which you can access the attic. Be aware that most attics lack a floor deck, so moving around inside the attic requires that you step only on the wooden joists to avoid crashing through the ceiling below.

For this investigation, you need not climb into the attic. However, when inspecting the attic, **wear eye protection, such as a pair of wrap-around safety glasses, as well as respiratory protection.** Use your flashlight and look through the opening into the space.

Animals

As you open the attic, be aware of any odours. A musty smell indicates dampness. An ammonia-like smell may indicate the presence of animals. Pigeons and bats can be very hazardous when they roost in attics because several fungi live in their droppings that cause infectious diseases in people. If you find birds or bats roosting in an attic or elsewhere, consider getting professional assistance to remove them and clean up their mess.

Air leakage into the attic

Air leakage into the attic from the house can cause condensation on cool surfaces in the attic space during winter, leading to mold growth and can also lead to ice damming. Installing roof vents is not the solution. Leaks from the house should be sealed.

Roof leaks

Shine your flashlight on the underside of the roof. Look for stains that may indicate water leaks. If it is winter, look for ice. Make careful note of the condition of points where the roof bends or changes direction, as these are sensitive areas for leaks. In extreme circumstances, you may need to remove ice from your roof to prevent damage due to water infiltration or structural stress, or personal injury from falling ice.

The CMHC publication *About Your House: Removing Ice on Roofs,* 62036 provides step-by-step instructions on how to do this safely.

Insulation

The current building codes require attic roof insulation between R31 and R40 depending on the climatic data and known temperature patterns. The insulating properties vary from material to material, but glass fibre insulation should be in the range of 220 mm thick to provide R31. Look for any signs of water damage, especially around light fixtures where air leakage is common. Insulation should not restrict air movement. If the insulation is fiberglass or rock wool, it should be loose and fluffy. Water damage can cause fluffy insulation to become compressed, which reduces its insulating capacity.

APPENDIX C:
PREVENTING MOISTURE PROBLEMS

This section provides a general guide to identifying when and what to fix in order to reduce the risk of moisture damage that could lead to mold growth. A careful and handy homeowner can perform many of these tasks but must take precautions to ensure safety.

We do not spell out here all the details of work to perform. Please be advised that inexperienced do-it-yourselfers should not attempt some of the major repairs but instead should hire professional contractors.

KEY PRINCIPLES

For your home, the process of preventing moisture problems should be ongoing, repetitive and relatively simple, and should follow these key principles:

- Regular checks
- Corrective maintenance
- Routine maintenance
- Life-cycle renewal or replacement of major components

If you are performing this investigation for the first time, there are likely quite a number of items which must be addressed or corrected immediately. But once the initial repairs are performed, the ongoing maintenance type of repairs and renewals should be reasonably manageable and predictable.

Regular checks

Make your checks a continual or regular procedure. As a rule of thumb, you should inspect your home yearly. We recommend that a full investigation be carried out at least once every five years. If you are not comfortable on ladders or in attics, consider hiring a qualified professional. Regularly check the following items:

Exterior

- Roof
  - Leakage
  - Ice damming
- Eaves, eavestroughs and downspouts
- Chimney
- Flashings
- Cladding/siding
- Windows
- Sealants
- Foundation walls
- Grading and drainage

Interior

- Interior sides of exterior walls
- Windows
- Ceilings
- Floors and flooring
- Floor drains
- Sump
- Furnishings and stored items
  - Living space
  - Laundry area
  - Storage space
  - Hobby areas

Mechanical systems
  - Heating and cooling systems
  - Humidifier/dehumidifier
  - Plumbing
- **Exhaust ventilation**
  - Dryer, range hood, bathroom fans
- **Attic**
  - Air leakage
  - Insulation
- **Miscellaneous**
  - Aquarium tanks, houseplants, etc.

Corrective maintenance

The need for corrective maintenance may be identified during the yearly check and most likely after you complete your first investigation. Corrective measures involve repairing anything that is leaking or broken, since such problems introduce superfluous moisture into your house. These items include things like missing or cracked shingles, torn roof valleys, broken eavestroughs or downspouts, holes in the roof, unsealed penetrations, broken windows, rotten window frames, missing sealants, holes in the cladding, inadequate grading leading to drainage problems, leaking faucets, sweating pipes, sweating toilets, leaking bathtubs, failed caulking at tubs or sinks, inadequate interior venting, poor attic venting, etc. All these items need correction first—before you can plan for regular maintenance and future renewals.

Sometimes you may even identify bigger items needing correction, including things like roofs that leak in the winter due to ice damming; or old windows that were improperly flashed and leak water through their frames into the interior; or simply roofs that are so old that they cannot be repaired. These problems can sometimes only be rectified through complete replacement or renewal.

Routine maintenance

Routine maintenance activities are generally simple housekeeping chores that can be performed on an ongoing basis throughout the year. These include activities like clearing eavestroughs; clearing and resetting downspouts; removing and resealing poor caulking, raking garden soil to proper grade (sloping away from your house); washing bathroom walls, cleaning condensation drains, cleaning ceilings and shower curtains, cleaning exhaust grilles or louvers, cleaning/resetting humidifiers if you use them, reorganizing storage of papers and clothing, etc.

Renewals or replacements

Ongoing maintenance will help you recognize problems before major building components actually fail. For example, timely replacement of shingles would avoid costly mold remediation that could result from a roof leak.

Regular checks performed diligently help not only to identify areas requiring maintenance but also help to determine the best time at which to replace each important component.

Flooding

Flooding requires a rapid and precise response to prevent disastrous consequences. How a flood should be handled is determined, in part, by what form of water caused the damage (for example, burst supply water pipe, storm water or sewage). If you have had a flood, it is urgent, even critical, that the process of cleaning up the water be essentially completed within 48 hours of the flood. Some of the procedures outlined in this guide may apply to cleaning up a flood. However, a detailed discussion of flood clean-up procedures is well beyond the scope of this guide. The CMHC guide *Cleaning Up Your House After A Flood,* 61094 provides advice to people who have experienced water damage as a result of flooding.

APPENDIX D: PRINT RESOURCES

INDOOR ENVIRONMENT AND HEALTH

General Audience

Canada Mortgage and Housing Corporation (CMHC). 1997. *The Clean Air Guide: How to Identify and Correct Indoor Air Problems in Your Home, 61082,* Catalogue No. NH15-83/1998E, 34 pp.

> A must for anyone who suffers from allergy or asthma, this book will help you to make your environment less disruptive to your health. The workbook guides users through an investigation of their indoor environment and provides practical tips that can be easily implemented, many immediately, to improve indoor air quality and health.

CMHC. 1994. *Cleaning Up Your House After a Flood,* 61094, 39 pp.

> During the first 48 hours after a flood, a number of critical steps must be taken and completed in order to prevent costly and hazardous problems. This book guides you step-by-step through this process and is essential for those who find themselves ankle-deep after a flood.

CMHC. 1992. *Investigating, Diagnosing and Treating Your Damp Basement,* 61065, 124 pp.

> This practical guide delivers exactly what the title promises. It is well-written, although concise in parts, and extensively illustrated with good diagrammatical cutaways that provide visual clarification of difficult concepts. The provided fold-out summary page of basement problems and solutions is great. This guide is an excellent companion to *Clean-Up Procedures for Mold in Houses.*

May, J. 2001. *My House Is Killing Me.* Baltimore, Maryland: Johns Hopkins University Press, 338 pp.

> This handsome, cloth-bound book provides an excellent overview of indoor air quality issues affecting health in a domestic environment. It draws on the author's extensive experience of conducting home investigations. The information is presented conversationally in case-studies. It is highly informative, insightful, well-written and entertaining to read.

Technical—Academic Resources

Dillon, H.K., P.A. Heinsohn and J.D. Miller, eds. 1996. *Field Guide for the Determination of Biological Contaminants in Environmental Samples.* Fairfax, Virginia: American Industrial Hygiene Association (AIHA), 174 pp.

> The so-called "AIHA Field Guide" (1996 or current edition) is the standard manual for professionals conducting investigations into problems involving environmental microbes. It presents industry-standard methods for collecting, analysing and interpreting environmental microbes (mainly bacteria and fungi). However, little discussion is given to health considerations.

Flannigan, B. and P.R. Morey, eds. 1996. *Control of Moisture Problems Affecting Biological Indoor Air Quality.* Ottawa, Ontario: International Society of Indoor Air Quality and Climate (ISIAQ) Guideline TFI-1996, 70 pp.

This book is a good technical resource for understanding and solving moisture problems in residential buildings. Its emphasis is on controlling moisture and, as such, there is really no meaningful discussion directly pertaining to mold.

Flannigan B, Samson RA, Miller JD (eds; 2001). *Microorganisms in Home and Indoor work Environments: Diversity, Health Impacts, Investigation and Control.* Taylor & Francis, London. 490 pp.

This book provides information on the characteristics of molds that grow in the built environment including in Canada, health information, and information on some of the fungi with excellent colour photographs and micrographs of the fungi concerned.

Macher, J., ed. 1999. *Bioaerosols: Assessment and Control.* Cincinnati, Ohio: American Conference of Governmental Industrial Hygienists (ACGIH), 331 pp.

This book is one of the best all-round technical resources for professionals dealing with indoor air quality problems relating to molds and other microbes. It is well written and organized and provides balanced overviews of many complex issues, including health effects (as far as current knowledge extends). It remains a good state-of-the-art reference on indoor microbes.

Samson, R.A., B. Flannigan, M.E. Flannigan, A.P. Verhoeff, O.C.G. Adan and E.S. Hoekstra, eds. 1994. *Health Implications of Fungi in Indoor Environments.* Air Quality Monographs, Vol. 2 . Amsterdam, The Netherlands: Elsevier, 602 pp.

This volume is a compilation of papers presented at an international expert workshop (of the same title) held in the Netherlands in November 1992. Despite the fact that the work is rather dated (particularly the papers dealing with health effects), much of the general discussion is still relevant. The text is well written and edited but highly technical and of little use to non-academics. It is also astronomically priced. If you live close to a university library that holds this volume, it may be worthwhile to borrow it and read a couple of the introductory papers (there is a particularly excellent paper here by Drs. Brian Flannigan and J. David Miller).

GENERAL MYCOLOGY

Kendrick, W.B. 2001. *The Fifth Kingdom,* 3rd edition. Mycologue Publications.

Review of the second edition in the international mycological journal, *Mycotaxon:* "… the sportiest, most engaging, most comprehensive and current, and most reasonably priced text on the market … Most chapters have been noticeably revised … My overall impression is that while the revised edition retains the singular Kendrickian flair … it is a more serious and comprehensive treatment … In provocatively conveying the multitude of ways that fungi impact the ecosystem, and particularly human affairs, this text has no equal as an introduction to mycology." The third edition remains at the top of its field and is a must for anyone interested in fungi.

Gams, W., E.S. Hoekstra and A. Aptroot, eds. 1998. CBS *Course on Mycology,* 4th ed. Centraalbureau voor Schimmelcultures (CBS): Utrecht, the Netherlands. 165 pp.

This text is the companion to the long-standing and popular CBS course on mycology. It covers many of the basics in a logical and readable format.

APPENDIX E:
INTERNET RESOURCES

The rapid increase in Internet use in Canada has made Canadians one of the most connected populations in the world. Many Canadians are able to use Internet to research topics of interest, without having to visit their local library or consult experts directly. As a result of Internet, the public has access to a fantastic amount of valuable information on an unlimited number of topics. Unfortunately, the great ease of Internet publishing has simultaneously made available a vast amount of unsubstantiated and even false or misleading information. As such, critical evaluation is essential when using information obtained online. Some questions to bear in mind when evaluating any information you encounter:

- To whom is information attributed? An individual or organization? What is their credibility?

- Has the information been substantiated or sanctioned by other members of the community who are recognized as experts?

- Is the information provided as marketing material for products or services?

- How current is the information? If it is an older reference, has it been recently re-evaluated or substantiated?

SOME USEFUL LINKS . . .

Indoor molds

Health Canada *Fungal contamination in public buildings: Health effects and investigation methods* Bilingual, retrieved July, 2004 from:
http://www.hc-sc.gc.ca/hecs-secs/air_quality/pdf/fungal_contamination.pdf

U.S. Environmental protection Agency (EPA) *Indoor air—Mold* English only, retrieved June, 2004 from:
http://www.epa.gov/mold/

New York City Department of Health and Mental Hygiene *Guidelines on assessment and remediation of fungi in indoor environment* English only, retrieved June, 2004 from:
http://www.ci.nyc.ny.us/html/doh/html/epi/moldrpt1.html

Canadian Construction Association (CCA) CCA82—*Mould guidelines for the Canadian construction industry* Bilingual, retrieved June, 2004 from:
http://www.cca-acc.com/mould/index/html

Molds and health

Board on Health Promotion and Disease Prevention (HPDP) Institute of Medicine (IOM) *Damp indoor spaces and health* English only, retrieved July, 2004 from
http://www.nap.edu/books/0309091934/html/

Institute of Medicine (IOM) *Clearing the air: Asthma and indoor air exposures* English only, retrieved July, 2004 from
http://www.nap.edu/books/0309064961/html/

Mold biology and general mycological resources

University of Toronto, Department of Botany, *Moulds: Isolation, cultivation and identification* English only, retrieved July, 2004 from
http://www.botany.utoronto.ca/ResearchLabs/MallochLab/Malloch/Moulds/Moulds.html

Cornell University, *The WWW virtual library: Mycology; On-line mycological reference* English only, retrieved July, 2004 from
http://www.doctorfungus.com

Cleaning up after birds and bats (Histoplasmosis/Cryptococcosis)

Health Canada *Effective control of bats* Bilingual, retrieved July, 2004 from
http://www.hc-sc.gc.ca/pmra-arla/english/pdf/pnotes/bat-e.pdf

National Institute for Occupational Safety and Health (NIOSH) and the National Center for Infectious Diseases (NCID), Centers for Disease Control and Prevention *Histoplasmosis: Protecting workers at risk* retrieved July, 2004, from
http://www.cdc.gov/niosh/hi97146.html

APPENDIX F:
TESTING RESOURCES

MOLD TESTING

In dealing with mold problems, the issue of laboratory testing frequently comes up. In general, however, mold testing for small-scale mold problems is not recommended for homeowners for several reasons:

- The cleanup methods used do not vary according to the type of mold present. Thus, the cleanup procedures described in this Guide are suitable for all kinds of mold as long as the affected area does not exceed 3 m² (30 sq. f.). Health Canada and other authorities state that mold growth needs to be removed under safe conditions, followed by a thorough particulate cleaning and that the underlying moisture problem needs to be corrected, regardless of the types of fungi present.

- Mold testing can be an expensive and time-consuming endeavour. The money you would spend on laboratory tests may be better spent hiring a professional investigator or fixing the problem.

- A thorough, building science-based investigation of the home for indoor air quality problems is more useful than mold testing. Mold tests do not identify the sources of moisture, why the problem occurred or what remedial measures are needed. A trained investigator identifies the causes and proposes appropriate remediation and repair strategies. Experienced investigators can also quantify mold damage and this is known to relate to the concentrations of mold in the air. Such signs include visible mold, moldy odours, history of flooding or leaks, and so on.

- Knowing the type of mold present does not tell you how great the hazard is. The hazard depends on two things:
  1) the type of mold
  2) the potential for you to be exposed to it.
  A laboratory can only tell you what the mold is, but cannot tell you about the hazard. A determination of the extent of the mold and moisture damage is a critical piece of information to assess health risk. Interpretation guidelines for laboratory tests are intended only to help professionals determine the existence and magnitude of indoor mold growth sites. At present, no agency has advocated "safe levels" of indoor molds.

On the other hand, there may be some valid reasons for mold testing. If you are uncertain about what you are calling "mold," you might be wise to have a sample (a scraping of a moldy surface, an imprint on cellophane tape or a piece of the moldy material) examined by a laboratory before mounting an expensive or disruptive cleanup. It might be worth the cost. Many materials such as candle soot and concrete efflorescence can, under certain conditions, seem like mold. If you have a health problem that may be related to mold in your house, your physician may request that you have samples analysed.

Many people who ask to have their house tested for mold usually have in mind that an air sample will be taken and sent to a laboratory. Testing the air for molds in single family dwellings and similar buildings is not recommended as a good first step by CMHC, the U.S. Environmental Protection Agency (EPA) or the American Industrial Hygiene Association. However, air testing may be indicated after the initial investigation for a number of reasons: mold is suspected but no mold can be seen, or there is a question whether a moldy area is affecting other occupied spaces. Testing may also be required as part of a legal case. If you are advised to have air samples tested for mold:

- Ensure that the investigator has the appropriate equipment and follows sampling methods from the American Industrial Hygiene Association. Your housing inspector may or may not be able to perform this sampling but should be able to provide a recommendation. The person conducting the sampling, not the laboratory, is required to provide interpretation of results.

- Ask the house investigator about the laboratory that will analyse the samples. Ensure that this laboratory is recommended either by your Medical Officer of Health, the public health department of your province or territory or is one of the laboratories used by the federal government.

- Spore counts or "colony forming units" alone have little or no value. A laboratory test identifies the types of molds that are present. The molds can be identified to genus (family) or to species. Identification to genus is less expensive but less informative—you may be told you have Penicillium, but you don't know which type of Penicillium. This can matter because some types grow on food and others can grow on building materials.

- At least two air samples should be taken at different times (early morning and evening) for each area of concern in the house.

- Samples taken outdoors are used for comparison. A significant proportion of mold(s) found indoors not present in concurrent outdoor samples usually means that there is an indoor source of mold that requires investigation and remediation.

- Air sampling alone provides no information on health risk.

A special case - apartment dwellers/rental housing

Large apartment buildings can have complicated mechanical ventilation systems that make these structures more like office buildings than homes. Mold investigations in such buildings require people with different expertise than for smaller buildings. Air sampling is more commonly done in large buildings and the principles discussed above apply. For small or older apartment buildings or rental housing, the local public health department should be contacted for information on the assistance it can provide to tenants.

TESTING LABORATORIES

Mold testing is difficult and requires specialized expertise. Not all environmental testing laboratories have adequate resources to do this type of work. The laboratory should have experience and demonstrated performance in the identification of environmental mold. The laboratory can provide advice and references towards the development of the sampling strategy, including test methods, equipment and media, sampling time, transportation, and analysis and reporting period.

The laboratory should meet the following criteria:

- The analytical staff should have training and experience in the identification of environmental mold and bacteria and should be able to identify mold to the species level.

- The laboratory should follow current best practices for environmental microbiology.

- The laboratory should be able to demonstrate successful participation in an external proficiency-testing program, wherein the laboratory periodically analyses test samples.

- The laboratory should have a comprehensive quality assurance program and designated quality assurance officer.

The person submitting the samples must complete a chain of custody form to accompany all samples. A unique identifier is assigned to each sample and clearly marked on the sample's packaging. Where available, the laboratory's own form should be used. Ensure that all applicable fields are completed, including sample number, type of analysis requested, date of collection and the date by which results are required. The form should be signed and dated every time the sample changes hands.

The analysis of biocontaminants other than molds requires specialized analyses that may be available from only a few laboratories.

ACKNOWLEDGMENTS

This second edition of *Clean-up procedures for mold in houses* is adapted and expanded from the first edition written by Jim White of CMHC.

Dr. Virginia Salares of CMHC and Dr. J. David Miller of Health Canada provided many suggestions and improvements to early drafts of this book.

CMHC thanks Dr. Mark Finklestien of Toronto for editorial assistance.

John Pogacar of Anderson Building Science, Toronto, kindly commented on moisture problems relating to building envelope deficiencies.